COME YEW ON, TERGETHER!

KEEP A-GOIN'

If it rain or if it snow
Keep a-goin',
If it hail or if it blow
Keep a-goin',
Tent no use t' set an' whine
Cors a fish ent on yar line,
Bait yar hook an' keep a-tryin'
Keep a-goin'.

(From a Victorian book of Norfolk Gleanings.)

COME YEW ON, TERGETHER!

A Rich Crop of Norfolk Dialect Writing

Selected and edited by

Keith Skipper

Come Yew On, Tergether!

Copyright © Keith Skipper, 2011

First published in 2011 by

Mousehold Press
Victoria Cottage
Constitution Opening
Norwich, NR3 4BD

www.mousehold-press.co.uk

ISBN 978-1-874739-61-6

CONTENTS

AUTHOR'S ACKNOWLEDGEMENTS:

A large cardboard box languishing in a corner of my cluttered study began to brim over with dialect delights. That was the spur for a marathon session of sifting and sorting to produce this long overdue volume dedicated to our glorious vernacular.

My passion for collecting such material has its roots in youthful renditions to family and friends of Boy John Letters cut out of the *Eastern Daily Press*. Happily, my years as local journalist, broadcaster and entertainer brought countless opportunities to continue along the same cheerful trail, meeting a proud band of fellow enthusiasts along the way.

When I first mooted the idea of an anthology like this the best part of some time ago, several leading exponents immediately presented written permission to include samples of their work, Ida Fenn, Maurice Woods, Cyril Jolly, Colin Riches and John Kett among them.

Gratitude to them is now extended to more recent willing scribes like Tony Clarke, Michael Brindid, Elizabeth Austrin and Sir Arnold Wesker, along with lively colleagues ploughing their fertile furrows with Friends Of Norfolk Dialect, the body I helped set up in 1999, and my Press Gang troupe of stage performers.

For strong pictorial support I salute Hilda Jolly, John Kett's family, Alan Howard, Jeremy and Esme Bagnall-Oakeley, Beryl Tooley, Jenny Comper, Rosemary Dixon, Lin Bensley, Ray Spinks and many others ready to back a special cause.

I am deeply indebted to two of Norfolk's most influential figures in print and on the local hustings, *Eastern Daily Press* editor Peter Waters and linguistics legend Peter Trudgill, for signposting these dialect adventures with words of wisdom and support.

Publisher Adrian Bell of the Mousehold Press has played a key role in bringing a proudly parochial project to fruition at last. His enthusiasm and expertise lifted my hoarding instincts out of the shadows.

I thank my wife Diane for her customary inspiration and organisation and our sons Danny and Robin for asking often enough when that "gret ole box up the corner" might yield a worthwhile result.

Well, here we are my bewties, a rich celebration of proper Norfolk writing by proper Norfolk people.

Keith Skipper
Cromer, 2011

FOREWORD

One lunchtime not so long ago, standing at the bar of a well-heeled hostelry in that area of the county dubbed Chelsea-on-Sea by estate agents keen to massage prices vertically, I was introduced to a good ol' Norfolk boy, a veteran parishioner of more than 80 years.

'So you come in for a pint every day?' I asked him.

'No. Every other day.'

'Oh, why only every other day?'

'Cors my brother come in when I dunt.'

'Oh dear, don't you get on with your brother?'

'No, that ent that.'

'Okay. Then why do you only come on alternate days?'

To which he scratched his stubbled chin, pushed the flat cap off his brow, and replied, 'Simple... we're only got one boike.'

Norfolk would be a poorer place without our characters, our humour and dialect. In an increasingly homogenised world, where sandwiches and coffee are bought from the same outlets throughout the world, and pub and restaurant chains proliferate, we should celebrate our identity and our uniqueness.

So it's refreshing that in this far-flung corner of our Sceptred Isle we have people like Skip who are unabashed in their championing of our pride at being different. In the face of encroaching Estuary English, Skip is a man not afraid to say 'Hold yew hard there, my ol' bewty'.

On the pages of the *Eastern Daily Press* we try to play our part in keeping alive our cultural heritage through our columnists, Tony Hall's cartoons, on our letters pages and through republishing dialect articles from the archives. That, I believe, is an important function of the EDP, a newspaper that seeks to be a daily affirmation of our wise decision to live in this beautiful county, whether you're indigenous or an incomer.

Norfolk's dialect is a voice that takes off its coat, rolls up its sleeves, spits on its hands and gets to work. It is certainly not one that might make people think a crèche is something that happens on the A11 at Elveden. But it's authentic, and it's ours. And we should hold on to that.

Peter Waters

Editor, *Eastern Daily Press*

Peter Waters, Editor, *Eastern Daily Press*

INTRODUCTION

Norfolk's very own Peter Trudgill is one of the world's leading authorities on dialects and at the heart of the campaign to defend them against prejudice and grim forecasts of extinction.

He has been honorary president of Friends Of Norfolk Dialect since the organisation was set up in 1999.

Born in Norwich, where he attended the City of Norwich School, he studied modern languages at King's College, Cambridge. He taught in the department of linguistic science at the University of Reading from 1970 to 1986 before becoming professor of sociolinguistics at the University of Essex.

He was professor of English language and linguistics at the University of Lausanne from 1993 to 1998 and after that at the University of Fribourg in Switzerland. He is now part-time professor of sociolinguistics at the University of Agder in Kristiansand, Norway, and adjunct professor at the research centre for linguistic typology at La Trobe University, Melbourne, as well as honorary professor at the University of East Anglia.

He is the ideal 'local lad', therefore, to set the scene for this celebration of the Norfolk vernacular...

Until recently, no one in Norfolk would've thought about writing in their local dialect. What I mean is – they wouldn't've thought about it because they would just've gone ahead and done it. That wasn't so very long ago that Horatio Lord Nelson was writing in his log that "Captain Lambert have been very fortunate" ... That was what everybody done in them days.

Speech come before writing. All the languages in the world was spoken long before they was ever written; and most of them still in't written down. Children learn to speak before they learn to write. And very many people in the world never learn to read and write at all. For nearly all of human history, there weren't no such thing as writing. Human language developed something like 100,000 years ago, but writing weren't invented until 95,000 years later.

When writing did first develop, what people naturally done was to write like what they spoke. What else were they a-going to do? Writing is just the representation of speech in a more permanent medium, and so they wrote down what they would've said if they had've been a-talking. But now a different practice have evolved. People are now encouraged *not* to write like what they speak – unless they come from the upper social classes. The upper classes speak Standard English as their native dialect; and the rest on us are encouraged to write in *their* dialect, not in our own. The idea seem to be that uniformity is a good thing. But this is a very new idea, and that in't totally obvious that that's a good one. That make for problems for children who have to learn to read and write in a kind of language that in't their own. And is it worth it? Whatever can be written in Standard English can be written in dialect too (as I'm trying to show here), so there in't no linguistic advantages to be gained neither.

Happily, though, there are still lots of places where writers feel free to use their natural vernacular speech forms, in the old way. Here in Norfolk, as Keith's book show, there continue to be a lot of writers what use their native dialect. We do have a long way to go before we get to the level of dialect use reached in Norway, where that's not at all unusual for serious novels and poetry to be written in dialect. But at least the writers what Keith present in this book have been doing their best – and very good that is too, specially when you think of the difficulties what they face.

The problems are pretty obvious. Local dialects are often looked down on as inferior – even though from a linguistic point of view they definitely in't. And writing in a local dialect is often considered to be eccentric – even though from a historical point of view that most certainly in't. So why do our dialect writers do it, then? Where do the impulse come from that all the writers what are eulogised in this here book by Keith Skipper have succumbed to? Of course there is a satisfaction in writing like what you speak. But publishing in the local dialect is a very symbolic activity too. To write in the Norfolk dialect demonstrate an affection for our part of the world; a respect for it; and a feeling of belonging that so many other people elsewhere haven't got no longer. That also signal a desire to preserve our heritage, and cherish our roots. Our dialect, like all dialects, is changing. But that's still alive and well, even if that do tend to run away and hide sometimes – some speakers suffer from a very sad kind of inferiority complex. So what's great about our dialect writers is that they don't share that sense of inferiority. Instead, what they are a-telling on us is that the dialect is something to celebrate; and they encourage all on us to continue to speak it.

Of course, using the dialect can be fun too. Dialect writing don't *have* to be comic. Serious Norwegian authors write in dialect because their dialects get a lot more respect than what English dialects do. That's why the work of writers like our novelist Mary Mann is so valuable. But Norfolk dialect-writing is also important because that portray and employ that very vital part of our local culture, our humour. And there's plenty of that in this here book.

In spite of the humour in these pages, though, Keith Skipper's book is also deadly serious, in its way. The Norfolk dialect do still survive, in spite of generations of dire predictions to the contrary. But all over the world, indigenous cultures and languages are dying out. If we don't do our best to defend our own culture, take pride in it, and defend it against ignorant prejudice – then no one else won't neither. Our Norfolk dialect need defending; and our dialect writers are playing a vital role in that defence.

Peter Trudgill

Mardling companions

PRECIOUS STRAND

What do Sir Thomas Browne, Prince Louis-Lucien Bonaparte, John Knowlittle, Lilias Rider Haggard, The Singing Postman and Sir Arnold Wesker have in common?

Well, they all line up as leading supporters of the long-running campaign to preserve and promote a precious strand of Norfolk's 'dew diffrunt' mantra amid the encroaching uniformity of English life.

They all cry 'Hold yew hard!' and call up a host of kindred spirits to help them keep aloft a wonderfully distinctive local tongue way above the 'charming little anachronism' level. They salute a vibrant cultural heritage untroubled by passing fancies. They point to a defiant future for something given up for dead nearly two centuries ago – and many times since.

This is an overdue celebration of Norfolk dialect writing, an occasionally perplexing and often contentious form of enlightenment and entertainment simply because there are no hard and fast rules in committing phonetics to print. (If there were, it would have to be 'fonetics' for a start ...).

As much of the material has been composed to be read out loud at social gatherings, some would claim the spelling doesn't really matter. Even so, it can be a bit disconcerting to find the same word or expression given two or three different treatments in the same paragraph or verse. There should be a limit to this Norfolk licence to talk as you like and spell as you please!

Despite the problems of spelling, difficulties in using a limited vocabulary and being confronted with questions of how to indicate intonation, Norfolk dialect enthusiasts from all walks of life continue to offer their unique versions in stories, anecdotes, letters and poems. There can be no doubt that this sort of homely literature, both light-hearted and more serious, comes from the heart.

Perhaps there's also more than a hint of that much-vaunted streak of cussedness running through the entire canon of home-made Norfolk writing. Why, even the most ardent champions of the parochial pen have been known to argue cogently against their own instincts and talents.

Dick Bagnall-Oakeley, one of the 20th century's most colourful and gifted local personalities as teacher, naturalist and broadcaster, claimed in the early 1970s that Norfolk could not be written down:

> Its accents and vowel sounds are too subtle, too varied and too rich for the alphabet which suffices for the rest of the English tongue.
>
> Sometimes you will see somebody making an attempt at the impossible, written Norfolk – the capture of broad Norfolk in an alphabet of a mere 26 letters.

Happily, Dick managed to defy all those restrictions to leave a rich series of Norfolk tales and a glowing reputation for being one of the first names mentioned when enthusiasts gather to chat about local dialect and its inherent humour.

About 40 years earlier, Russell Colman, then serving as Lord Lieutenant of Norfolk, provided a foreword for B. Knyvett Wilson's *Norfolk Tales and Memories*, in which he confessed:

> I have never experienced any difficulty in speaking 'Norfolk', but – quite frankly – I do not know how to write it. If I have not forgotten my schoolboy lessons, there are five vowels and sometimes two extra. For 'Norfolk' that does not appear to me to be anything like what I require. Take the following sentence and render it into 'Norfolk'; 'There's nothing ever goes down that old driftway, unless it be a farm-cart.' There's *northen* ever go down that *ood* driftway *doo* that's only a *farm-cart.'*
>
> Now, in all the five words I have italicized I want a fresh supply of vowels and unless I may have them I can't write 'Norfolk'.

For all the Lord Lieutenant's misgivings, he knew this batch of endearing Norfolk tales and memories sprang from deep wells of affection and creativity and that it would inspire many more to be collected, jotted down, shared and cherished.

Max Muller, writing in the *Eastern Daily Press* well over a century ago, seemed to have worked out why people felt a deep desire to create in their own local languages:

The real and natural life of language is in its dialects. Even in England the local patois have many forms which are more primitive than the language of Shakespeare, and the richness of their vocabulary surpasses on many points that of the classical writers of any period.

The dialect has lasted best in more isolated areas – Norfolk's geography has bequeathed an independence that has shaped character and helped protect it – although some dialect speakers and scribes are 'bilingual'. They speak the local vernacular within their own communities but switch to Standard English for the benefit of outsiders or when away from their own home. This brand of versatility will become more pronounced.

Indeed, it was evident in the 1890s when Thomas Hardy captured the state of affairs well in *Tess of the d'Urbervilles* as he wrote:

Mrs Durbeyfield habitually spoke the dialect; her daughter, who had passed the Sixth Standard in the National School under a London-trained mistress, spoke two languages – the dialect at home, more or less, ordinary English abroad and to persons of quality.

The supreme irony, of course, is that many blessed supporters featured in this celebration assumed they were simply launching a final flourish in spotlighting their glossaries and other fond salutes to the local tongue.

Pointing to popular dialects in his introduction to *The Vocabulary of East Anglia* compiled in the early 1800s, the Rev. Robert Forby lamented: 'Will they not be overwhelmed and borne down by the general onset of the various plans and unwearied exertions for the education of all?'

Harry Cozens-Hardy, who edited the first *Broad Norfolk* booklet published in 1893 from letters sent to the *Eastern Daily Press*, prophesied the dialect would die out within a generation under the influence of the Board Schools.

Over half-a-century later, a second *Broad Norfolk* collection featured over 400 letters on the same subject. Eric Fowler, who wrote for the *EDP* with such flair and distinction under the pen-name of Jonathan Mardle, wove them into a compelling volume which proved 'the remains of the Norfolk dialect in 1949 are still substantial, and that literacy has rather amplified than killed the delight of Norfolk people of possessing their own turn of speech.'

However, he did feel as if he had just chronicled yet another phase in the decline of Broad Norfolk – but warned against more rash prophesies about its extinction. Good move, ole bewty ... as his 1973 offering under the same name underlined. He ended that third version of *Broad Norfolk* with a clarion call worthy of repeat whenever someone musters enough audacity to suggest dialect days must be numbered:

I should like true Norfolk to survive because of its expressive vocabulary and vivid turn of phrase – so much more vigorous (and honest) than the gobbledegook of the bureaucrats and sociologists, with which we are nowadays so smothered that the language itself is in danger of losing its meaning. The English country dialects, if they do indeed remain alive, may well become the last repository – outside of old books – of good plain English.

It is remarkable how two particular 'callings' dominate our cast in this tribute to 'true Norfolk' – the Church and the Press. Yes, the pulpit and the pen, the preacher and the scribe, stand out strongly among those soaked in Norfolk ways, speech and humour.

Perhaps well-educated country parsons like Robert Forby and Edward Gillett had enough spare time after orthodox clerical duties to tune in, jot down and savour local words and expressions they feared would be washed away with the advance of education and improved communications. They used that time expertly, however, and also cultivated useful contacts to widen their collections and push the Norfolk cause further afield. We owe them a big debt, not least for encouraging 20th century men of the cloth and several lay preachers to add their valuable chapters to a proud survival story.

My close working links with local newspapers since leaving school in 1962 must not be treated as an automatic personal switch for paeans of praise towards all journalists and contributors bright enough to share my passion for our gloriously resilient dialect. It would have been just the same had I become a long-distance lorry driver, short-term investment banker or middle-of-the-road record producer. The role of our press in encouraging, enhancing and extending the vernacular cause cannot be overstated.

James Spilling, second editor of the *Eastern Daily Press*, set a prolific example with a series of sketches in dialect between 1870 and 1890, including the trailblazing *Giles's Trip to London*. It was an immediate hit and went on to sell in its hundreds of thousands.

Sidney Grapes, garage proprietor and established Norfolk comedian, penned the humorous Boy John Letters to the *EDP* between 1946 and 1958. They soon became the most regularly quoted examples of our local dialect among natives and exiles alike and remain strong favourites today.

Naturalist Arthur Patterson, performing under the splendidly self-effacing pseudonym of John Knowlittle, contributed Melinda Twaddle's Notions to the *Yarmouth Mercury* for over 30 years. Ida Fenn later graced the same journal with her Tales of a Countryman for more than two decades. Maurice Woods, a former London editor of the *EDP*, sent Harbert's News from Dumpton to the local weekly papers for almost 40 years. These labours of love were hardly short-term assignments.

There have been many other whimsical and witty contributors to an ever-popular genre while the formation of Friends Of Norfolk Dialect in 1999 sparked a fresh surge of enthusiasm for both written and spoken projects.

I have arranged this roll of honour roughly in chronological order to show how certain themes and ways of highlighting them have fed a following generation of willing exponents. For example, writers from different centuries and vastly different backgrounds have been anxious to dispel the simpleton image of the rustic. The battle continues.

I have remained faithful to original spelling and uses of grammar and punctuation except where the original is so original that it confuses beyond a reasonable level of individuality.

While a homely and jocular touch ambles through much of the material on display, there is room for more 'serious' deployment of dialect by writers like Mary Mann, James Blyth and Lilias Rider Haggard.

A few sadly-neglected figures, such as Norwich city councillor and poet Charles Loynes Smith and puckish north Norfolk parson Charles Harold Fitch, make happy returns to a stage where there's always room for more. I am sure this volume must revive other reputations.

To prove I can practise what I try to preach I call up Old Barney, my 'alter ego' as rural correspondent for BBC Radio Norfolk over seven slow-pedalling years in the 1980s. Three volumes of his Saturday morning bulletins demonstrated how the pen and the microphone can play equally powerful roles in preserving and promoting that precious strand in years to come.

This is not an clegy. It would be foolish to tread in the same doubts and fears that have bedevilled so many 'last-gasp' supporters over two centuries.

It is a eulogy. It would be downright churlish to offer anything other than highest praise to every dialect disciple who has bothered to write down a contribution to the 'dew diffrunt' gospel.

Now let it ring loud and strong throughout the 21st century and beyond.

FOOD FOR THOUGHT

In Norfolk, it is unusual for a farm hand to 'live in' with his master, though this is, of course, usual in the 'grass counties'. There was, however, one who did so live for many years near North Walsham. One day he came to his master and gave notice to leave, and after some inquiry he acknowledged that a neighbouring farmer had ''ticed' him away with an offer of another shilling or so per week. 'Well, John, I ain't one to stand in your way,' said his master; so off John went. After a month or two John returned and begged to be taken on again. 'Well,' said his old master, 'I ain't suited in your place, but why are you a-leavin' Mr—? Doan't they feed ye well?' 'Why, maaster, thass like this hare,' said old John. 'T'ree week ago th'ould sow died, an' we ate har; last week th'ould cow died, an' we ate har, *an now th'ould missus is dead!'*

ROOM FOR IMPROVEMENT

I heard of two Norfolk men who met in a tavern in the backwoods of Tasmania and were talking somewhat wistfully together of the Old Country. One of them had quoted, rather grandiloquently, Cowper's 'England with all thy faults I love thee still!' when a voice from the back interjected, 'Ah, dessay, an' old Norwich will be all right when they ha' widened Brigg Street!'

B. Knyvet Wilson, *Norfolk Tales and Memories*, 1930

Sir Thomas Browne ponders the local dialect

BROWNE'S LIST

It took one of Norfolk's most famous adopted sons, an exceptional scholar of his age, to first pay proper heed to the fact the place had a dialect all of its own.

Sir Thomas Browne, a writer and physician of prodigious talent, included love of language on his scroll of honours and passions. In the latter part of the 17th century he made a list in his tract, *Of Language, and particularly of the Saxon Tongue*, of 26 examples of 'words of no general reception in England but of common use in Norfolk.'

Browne spent most of his life in Norwich after years of study in Oxford and Europe. He settled in the city in 1637, married Dorothy Mileham and they had 12 children. He was knighted in 1671 by Charles 11 as a steadfast Royalist noted for his antiquarian scholarship, and died on his 77th birthday, October 19, 1682.

His prose, so rich in exotic coinage and striking imagery, is one of the most remarkable accomplishments in English literature, reckoned to be at its best when Browne treats themes that allow full display of his personality, such as religion in *Religio Medici* and oblivion in *Hydriotaphia*, or *Urn Burial*.

He became involved in the notorious Bury Witch Trial of 1662 when the judge asked for his expert opinion. Had the children been bewitched or not? Browne considered they had – and two old widows from Lowestoft were hanged four days later. The trial was thoroughly documented and quoted frequently as precedent during the Salem Witch Trials in Massachusetts in 1692.

Sir Thomas Browne's statue on Hay Hill in Norwich was unveiled in 1904. His memorial is nearby in the sanctuary of St Peter Mancroft Church. In 1840, while another grave was being prepared, his coffin was accidentally smashed open. His skull, hair and the broken coffin plate were removed and sold to a local chemist, Robert Fitch.

They were later acquired by a Dr Lubbock who presented the skull to the Norfolk and Norwich Hospital. It stayed there until after an undignified squabble over the cost, it was returned to St Peter Mancroft in 1922. It was reinterred in a specially made casket with full burial rites, which referred to it as being aged 317 years!

Back to that precious list of words, underlining how Browne had the capacity and interest to tune in to local voices and provide the first written record of the Norfolk dialect: bawnd, bunny, thurck, enemmis, sammodithee, mawther, kedge, seele, straft, clever, matchly, dere, nicked, stingy, noncare, feft, thepes, gosgood, kamp, sibrit, fangast, sap, cothish, thokish, bideowe and paxwax.

Some of these were obsolete or long out of fashion by the time Robert Forby's *Vocabulary of East Anglia* was published in 1830, but others lingered well into the 20th century. A select few still resonate with hardened enthusiasts: bunny (a bruise or swelling), clever (with its special meaning in Norfolk of handsome or dexterous), mawther (girl or young woman), seele (greeting, as in 'I gave him the seele o' the day'), stingy (cruel or mean), thepes, thapes or fapes (green gooseberries), sibrits (or sibits – banns of marriage) and paxwax (sinew in a joint of meat).

Browne also made the first mention in literature of the Norfolk Broads waterways – so that's an impressive double for a highly intelligent 'blow-in' of the 17th century!

While he was a Norfolk trailblazer, the good Sir Thomas had to yield national honours to Essex botanist John Ray. He produced the first dialect dictionary in print in 1674, *A Collection of English Words, Not Generally Used.*

Ray travelled extensively around England after the Restoration collecting material for his scientific research. He was struck by 'difference of dialects and variety of local words' in places he visited 'such as are not of general use'. He made a list but also solicited friends to send on 'what they had observed each of their own country words, or should afterwards gather up out of the mouths of the people.' Ray published a much expanded second edition of the dialect dictionary in 1691.

This method of gathering information from friends and correspondents all over the country became a key platform in the campaign to recognise and record proud local individuality – with Norfolk and its neighbours well to the fore.

JACK VALENTINE

I'd hear a tap upon ma door
I'd run ta see who's there
Instead a little parcel
Ud on this day appear.

My mum knew he was comun
My dad he'd disappear
I dint know what Jack looked like
An I dint really care.

He'd leave me sweets an crayons
Sometimes a little book.
An my Dad ud come in later
say he'd come ta hev a look.

He never called on orl ma friends
but allus come ta mine
On February 14th
My own Jack Valentine.

(Tina Chamberlain, *Um Stilla Thinkun*, 2007)

Rev.d Robert Forby.

Rector of Fincham Norfolk.

N. Sharpe fins.d 1833.

FORBY'S FEAST

If Thomas Browne's little list proved a tasty appetiser, Robert Forby's massive collection of local words and phrases has provided a veritable dialect feast for earnest scholars and enthusiastic amateurs alike over the best part of two centuries.

The Norfolk country parson never saw his pioneering work come to fruition. He died in 1825, five years before publication of his *Vocabulary of East Anglia*, 'an attempt to record the vulgar tongue of the twin sister counties, Norfolk and Suffolk, as it existed in the last 20 years of the 18th century, and still exists; with proof of its antiquity from etymology and authority.'

With over 2,000 words and phrases it is the biggest collection made and remains a constant source of reference and delight. Every local glossary since has been based on it. Forby suggested 'such collections are not only curious but useful and might be made of public and general interest.'

Born at Stoke Ferry in 1759, 'of respectable but far from opulent parents', he was educated at the free school in King's Lynn before moving on to Caius College, Cambridge, from where he graduated in 1781. Forby went into the Church and held livings at Horningtoft, Barton Bendish, Wereham and, finally, Fincham. He became Rector of Fincham in 1801, combining the duties of a parson with those of magistrate and tutor of private pupils, and stayed there the rest of his days.

He made a consuming hobby of what he called his 'Icenian Glossary', supplementing his own knowledge and research with notes from various correspondents in other parts of Norfolk, Suffolk and Essex.

Forby considered the main value of his collection to be as a record of a dialect bound to die out with the advance of education and the improvement of communications as he saw them, even during the Regency.

While Forby is rightly lauded for his collecting and organising, it is only fair to emphasise significant parts played by others in bringing to life the vocabulary bearing his name.

In the early 1800s, the Rev William Tylney Spurdens, a native of Suffolk, and a close friend, John Deere of Brundall, began a collection of what they called 'Icenisms'. They were hardly academic hoarders of words, but mopped them up in the field in the course of their sporting and social activities.

Through the Yarmouth antiquary Dawson Turner, Deere heard that Robert Forby was engaged in compiling a record of 'the vulgar tongue' of East Anglia. Showing commendable generosity, Spurdens and Deere agreed to make common cause with the Norfolk vicar.

Such teamwork is highlighted by my old friend Robert Malster in his dialect dictionary, *The Mardler's Companion*, published in 1999. He points out that the famous book resulting from the three men's work didn't appear until five years after Forby's death.

Another of Forby's collaborators was the Rev George Turner of Kettleburgh, near Framlingham, and it fell to him to edit material left by Forby. Turner admitted he was not always able to decipher parts of the manuscript that appeared to have been unfinished at the time of the author's death.

Turner seems to have been unaware of the participation of Spurdens and Deere in the gathering of material for Forby's book and no acknowledgement of their work appeared in the preface of the Vocabulary of East Anglia.

Some years after publication of the book carrying Forby's name, Spurdens, then living at North Walsham, produced a manuscript for a supplementary volume. He in turn died before his work could be published and it didn't appear until 1858.

In a long and learned introduction to his *Vocabulary of East Anglia*, Forby noticed some local peculiarities which are not so much part of the dialect as of local character and turn of phrase. For example, he noted the way of stringing words together into colourful adjectives, like a woman who appeared before his bench of magistrates to give evidence against a ne'er-do-well who had done a runner from Fincham, leaving several illegitimate children chargeable to the parish. The woman said he was a 'toss-potly, stuff-gutly, smoke-baccarly, starve-bastardly, whoremongerly wagabond.' So there!

Forby does give some indication that his vast collection of words and phrases running into two hefty volumes received support from others:

Some months ago, a few literary friends, acquainted with the existence and the nature of his (the author's) philological stores, repeated, with more earnestness, representations others made before, that by a little necessary preparation and arrangement they might be made no unacceptable offering to the public.

One of those friends, who had long amused himself by forming a similar collection, principally in the county of Suffolk, powerfully supported his representation by frankly communicating it. It will readily be conceived that the two collections in great measure coincided. The additions, however, this made to the original stock were very considerable.

Forby also noted the roles played by Sir Thomas Browne and John Ray in paving the way towards publication of his own stock of provincialisms. Even so, he took Browne mildly to task for not giving the derivation or meaning of any of his 26 words.

The good village parson set the trend for doom-laden forecasts about local voices, especially in rural areas, with the onset of education for all:

An apprehension exists, it seems, of present and pressing dangers to the permanence and the very existence of ours and all our popular dialects. They are imagined to be in a state of rapid decline and to be actually giving way to a more correct diction.

This great change is expected from the general disposition to acquire knowledge and the increased facilities of diffusing it among those who formerly rested humbly content in their ignorance.

These alarming indications have really been urged to the Author by some of his literary friends as inducements to arrange and publish his collection without delay, lest the peculiarities of our mother tongue, if not recorded in time, be irrecoverably lost.

A shade pompous and long-winded. A bit patronising. Yet his glossary remains a precious source of information and inspiration two centuries after Robert Forby's magpie instinct took hold.

FOG, *s.* long grass, growing in pastures, in late summer or autumn; not fed down, but allowed to stand through the winter, and yielding early spring feed. By its length and thickness, the outer part forms a cover or sort of thatch for the lower, which is kept fresh and juicy, at least through a mild winter. This seems to entitle it to sk. derivation, Ital. *affogare.* R. N. C. PE. W. C. BR.

FOGGER, *s.* a huckster; a petty chapman carrying small wares from village to village.

FOISON, *s.* succulency; natural nutritive moisture, as in herbage. Ex. " There is no *foison* in this hay." We do not use it in its general sense of abundance. It is sometimes most perversely mispronounced *poison!* Fr. *foison.* R. N. C. L. SC.

FOISONLESS, devoid of foison. SC. N.

FOKY, *adj.* bloated; unsound; soft and woolly. Ex. " a *foky* turnip,"

FOLD-PRITCH, *s.* a heavy pointed iron, to make holes in the ground to receive the toes of hurdles. A. S. *priccan,* pungere.

FOLLOW, *v.* to practice for a livelihood. Ex. " He *follow* jobbing, shoe-making, tailoring." If it be said that a man *follows* farming, or any more respectable occupation, it must be understood to be on a narrow scale. And in general, indeed, it seems implied that he is not very likely to overtake what he *follows.*

FOND, *adj.* luscious; fulsome; disagreeably sweet, in taste or in smell.

FOOTING, *s.* sum paid down; or sometimes an entertainment given, on entering upon a new office or situation.

A page from Forby's vocabulary

GOOD SIGN

A friend of mine shot a shelduck and asked a marshman if it were good to eat. The latter would not commit himself so far, but said, 'Well. Sir, yew should take and get an owd brick and put that inter the oven with yar owd shelduck, and when you kin git a fork inter that there owd brick yar owd shelduck'll be fit t'eat!'

FLOORED

'Let me see,' said a visitor to the old parish clerk. 'Do you have matins now in this church?' 'Noo, sir, noo, not now we doan't. We hev a linoleum right up the whole way as far as the altar!'

MASTER'S VOICE

The late Mr Howson, Head Master of Gresham's School, Holt, was anxious to eradicate the Norfolk dialect as far as possible. I believe he thought he had succeeded. One day, however, on coming into the classroom he found that tea, which was overdue, was not ready. He turned with some impatience to one of his head boys. 'Have that bell rung!' he said. The boy at once said, 'No, sir, that ha'ent; not yit that ha'ent.' Alas for culture!

B. Knyvet Wilson, *More Norfolk Tales and Memories*, 1931

Edward Gillett

FRENCH CONNECTION

One of the more unlikely chapters in the history of Norfolk dialect writing unfolded in the 1860s, starring a village clergyman and an exiled member of the Bonaparte family. An *entente cordiale* with a real difference!

The Rev Edward Gillett was caring for his flock in the small parish of Runham, a few miles from Great Yarmouth, when he received his well-deserved reward for setting The Song Of Solomon to a distinctive new tune. He turned the Authorised Version of this poetic book of the Bible into the Norfolk tongue, his work being printed along with translations from 23 other counties at the expense of Price Louis-Lucien Bonaparte.

The Song o' Sorlomun has to be voted a relatively successful venture despite Gillett's own admission that he was not acquainted with any suitable phonetic spelling with which to indicate the 'Norfolk drant'.

So how did he meet the exiled prince, a scholarly soul determined to show that not all Napoleons were busy being emperors or engaging in wars of conquest? It seems their paths crossed first after Edward graduated from Emanuel College, Cambridge, and became Vicar of Shipmeadow, near Beccles.

After an early failed marriage to a French nobleman, Princess Caroline Murat, grand-daughter of Napoleon's general, wed a Suffolk squire, John Garden of Redisham Hall. There's a magnificent monument to her in Ringsfield churchyard. It appears likely that Prince Louis visited his cousin at Redisham, met neighbours from surrounding villages and enjoyed the Gillett rendition of *The Song o Sorlomun* at an impromptu 'Night of Squit' with a cultural edge.

By the time Edward became incumbent at Runham, the prince's ambitious dialect publishing project was in full swing. It came to fruition in 1862 with 250 copies of the Norfolk version rolling off the press.

Gillett was already well known as an antiquarian and left a host of unpublished manuscripts when he died. His family placed them with the Norwich subscription library but a disastrous fire in August, 1898, destroyed his collection. Happily, a couple of notebooks used as reference points for a range of diverse subjects, including archaeology, botany and brick making, went for safe keeping into the Norfolk Record Office.

Born at Halvergate in 1819, Edward married in 1862 - the year of his celebrated appearance in print – but died six years later, leaving three little boys and a daughter yet to be born. His wife died only three years after that. They are buried in Halvergate churchyard.

Louis-Lucien Bonaparte, third son of Napoleon's brother, Lucien Bonaparte, was born in England in 1813, his family being interned temporarily after being captured by the British en route to America.

A philologist and politician, he spent his youth in Italy and didn't set foot in France until 1848, serving two brief terms in the Assembly before moving to London, where he spent most of the remainder of his life.

He set himself the goal of building the finest collection of books in the world on historical linguistics. His first intent was to obtain something on every European language and dialect but later widened the search to include all languages and dialects in the world. His collection of nearly 19,000 items suggested he came mighty close to fulfilling all ambitions.

He kept up a stream of correspondence with the many Bible translators whose works were published at his considerable expense. He received a Civil List pension in 1883 in recognition of his work on English dialects. He died in 1891.

In his introduction to *The Song o 'Sorlomun*, Edward Gillett highlighted one of the problems he faced:

From the constant use of the Bible by all who can read just above the lower orders, our dialect has received a perceptible Biblical colouring; consequently, much difficulty has been experienced in setting forth a portion of scripture in a dialect which differs less from scripture than from any other work in correct English.

Changing words completely rather than just tinkering with the spelling brought intriguing results. Words immediately noticeable in the following short extract are 'yar', 'smell' and ' mawther' used in place of 'thy', 'savour' and 'virgin'. Translation into Norfolk dialect needed a bit more than respelling certain key words, not least because some vocabulary was not used in 19th century Norfolk.

'Mawther' was a local term of address to all females – still used widely today – while the word 'virgin' simply would not have been used in the same sense.

For all that, the general structure of the Song remains much the same. Apart from an obvious exchange of grammatical terms like 'which is Solomon's' for the Norfolk treatment 'as is Sorlomun's' and inclusion of the extra pronoun following a name, as in 'The king he ha' browt me into his charmbers', the 1862 version is mainly an attempt to incorporate only the 'sound' of the Norfolk tongue.

The Song of Solomon

from the 1611 Authorised Version of the Bible

CHAPTER 1

The song of songs, which is Solomon's.

2. Let him kiss me with the kisses of his mouth: for thy love is better than wine.

3. Because of the savour of thy good ointments thy name is as ointment poured forth, therefore do the virgins love thee.

4. Draw me, we will run after thee: The king hath brought me into his chambers: we will be glad and rejoice in thee, we will remember thy love more than wine: the upright love thee.

The Song o' Sorlomun

translated into Norfolk dialect by Revd Edward Gillett.

CHAPTER 1

The song o'songs, as is Sorlomun's.

2. Lerr 'im kiss me with the kisses of his mouth: for yar love is better 'an wine.

3. Becaze o' the smell o' yar good intements, yar name is as intements pored out, therefoor du the mawthers love ye.

4. Dror me, we'll run arter ye: the king he ha' browt me into his charmbers: we'll be glad and rejice in ye; we'll remahmber yar love more 'an wine: the right-up love ye.

THET OWL MOWLE

He'd med four mounds alreddy
In a line acrawst thuh lawn
Oi carn't ketch thuh ole daavil
Wish he'd nevver a bin born.

He're cawst me sum trubble
Patchin' an' mendin' where he're bin
Thass orlrite him mearkin' holes
But he doan't fill 'em in.

Wun o' these daze oi'll ketch him
Oi'll put a stop tew him
He's arter wams oi know
Not on my lawn thow.

So oi sets me trap up
An' waite forrit tew spring
That did, but he got threw
An' now he's back agin.

('Norfolk Tales' by Bruther Will, 1981)

James Spilling

CAPITAL HUMOUR

James Spilling was an intellectual who knew the value of a homely and jocular touch. Pioneering work in the name of the *Eastern Daily Press* brought plenty of plaudits. He earned a wider celebrity, however, with extensive dialect writing.

This amounted to much more than a patronising pastime or whimsical self-indulgence. There were serious motives behind his rustic humour and some of them had been properly recognised and saluted way beyond Norfolk's boundaries before his death in 1897.

London newspapers praised his 'real and original literary powers', unlikely bouquets for a provincial pressman who handed out a fair bit of capital punishment when it came to satire dipped in the vernacular.

Giles's Trip to London, first and most successful of his humorous series, was singled out as 'not only the best example of the Norfolk dialect ever given to the world but also an admirable and spirited piece of farcical humour.'

These metropolitan medals shine brightly alongside his reputation as a key figure in the history of our local press.

Spilling was born in Ipswich and as a fiery young radical in the hungry 1840s he bought a pike in order to be ready for the coming revolution. But the pen proved to be his main weapon in future battles.

He cultivated a literary turn of mind on being apprenticed to a local printer and bookseller. He joined the *Suffolk Chronicle* and stayed for several years. The style and perception of his articles were noted by Dawson Rogers, first editor of the *Eastern Daily Press* when it was launched in 1870.

At Rogers' behest, James Spilling ventured over the border to join the staff of the *Norfolk News*. Meanwhile, the new morning paper in Norwich lost money for the first five years. Rogers departed to London to found a news agency – and it was left to Spilling to nurse the *EDP* into prosperity and authority.

When he died in harness in 1897 he was publishing four newspapers, the *EDP*, the *Eastern Evening News*, which he started in 1882, the *Norfolk News* and a second weekly, the *Eastern Weekly Press*, all of them from an office in Norwich's Museum Court. All the type was hand-set and the printing press driven by an antiquated steam engine.

There had been no obvious pointers to dialect delights in the offing. A gentle, scholarly and philosophical soul, Spilling tried to propagate the teaching of Swedish mystic Emanuel Swedenborg. His main literary output before his full-time newspaper career had been a volume of poems called *The Spirit of the Seasons* and a series of articles of religious and social topics.

Then between 1870 and 1890 he wrote 'Sketches in dialect in Eastern Counties stories in the language of the people', probably the most extended use of the vernacular that has been attempted.

Giles's Trip to London – A Norfolk Labourer's First Peep at the World, was an instant hit, going on to sell in its hundreds of thousands. Much of the amusement in Giles Hobbins' adventures as an innocent abroad stems from the ignorance displayed towards the other's world, not least in the manner of speech. It also underlines another favourite theme of this brand of entertainment, to dispel the simpleton image of the rustic.

London with its bright lights and sophisticated ways squares up to Norfolk's homely country life, a sharp contrast bound to dominate dialect writing ever since.

This collision of two worlds is also delightfully explored in *The Cockneys in the Country* and *'Arry and 'Arriet*, two subsequent offerings in Spilling's highly popular sequence. Echoes are still heard today as natives weigh up 'furriners', especially those with capital connections.

A rich mixture of affection and reverence prompted a telling forecast from a *Norfolk News* staff writer on Spilling's death: 'The fun in it [Giles's Trip] has no vein of cynicism or contemptuousness. James Spilling's bucolics are loveable *ingénues* with many homely virtues. They are a faithful type and as such they will long survive in the public regard.'

My renewed interest was sparked by the centenary of Spilling's death. The freshness of the humour, allied to general accessibility of the dialect, convinced me it would be worth asking Giles to take another peek at the big city.

Happily, Antony Jarrold, then head of Jarrold Publishing, agreed to supply the return ticket for publication of a facsimile edition in 1998, a gesture prompted to some degree by the Norwich family firm's original printing of Spilling's work. Edited by 'The Village Schoolmaster' and featured in instalments in the *EDP*, this series of dialect publications provided Jarrolds with one of its biggest success stories.

During my research into Spilling's career for a new introduction to *Giles's Trip to London*, I discovered genuine concern for the plight of 19th century agricultural labourers, a strand destined to take on darker and deeper significance in Norfolk writing at the turn of the century.

In the *Eastern Weekly Press*, Spilling poured out leaders, special articles of rural interest and stories dealing with country life and hardships of the labourers. Trade unionism was growing and Spilling was credited with employing humour to uphold the rights of agricultural workers as well as attempting to smooth away differences between master and man so much in evidence at the time when the sketches were written.

Yes, philanthropy had to be tempered by business acumen, but there can be no doubt that James Spilling held Giles and all his rural colleagues in very high regard.

If Spilling inspired much of the comic writing to follow, he must also be lauded for preparing the path for more serious dissertations when it became evident that, for all its seductive images, the Norfolk countryside was falling apart in the closing years of the 19th century.

Extracts from *Giles's Trip to London*, first published in book form in 1872:

On the way

Puer owd aunt Jane wot lived cook up at squire's died and left me a nice little round sum i' the bank. Well, I thowt I should like to spend some on it in goin' to see Sairey Tippens and a few o' the sights o' Lunnen. So I got a letter wrote, and towd Sairey, who wor a-living housemaid at one o' the nobs at Kensington, that I wor a-comin' to see her, and then I up and towd maaster that he must let me go for a waak. I said I had been cuped up here long enough athowt seein' more'n six mile outside the green, and he must let me go.

First glimpse

All Lunnun saamed to be gathered together, and to be rushing past as faast as ever they could. I wor wholly scared like. Arter a minute or tew, I say to myself, 'There must be a percession goin' paast, like the Oddfellows and Foresters wot go about the willage once a-yaar; I'll wait till they're all gone by.' I waited about ten minutes, and I could see no end on 'em, but they saamed to be gittin' more and more, and to be hurryin' on faaster and faaster – cabs and omnibuses, and men and women, and children wor all alike.

A helping hand

Arter I had bin a-standin' naarly half-a-hour, a little boy come up, and he say, 'Goin' to stand 'ere all day, guv'ner?' 'No,' I say, 'my little man; I want to be a-goin' but I'm waitin' till all these paaple are paast.' The little boy bust out a-larfin', and he say, 'Yow are precious green, guv'ner,' he say; 'where du yow want to go tu? Yow'd hev to wait till midnight afore they'd be all gone. I can show ye where ye want to go tu,' he say, 'if ye like.' 'Well,' I say, 'can ye raad?' 'Can the 'potamus at the Zoo swaller a half-quarten loaf and make nothin' on't?' he say. 'If you can raad, then,' I say, 'raad that, and yow'll see where I want to go tu.'

A capital ride

Wotever they give them things the name o' 'Hansom' for I dunno' to this day. Handsome they sartainly aint, with the driver stuck up behind there i' that ugly fashion. Nayther du I call 'em comfortable, for ye git cramped up a-settin' in 'em with hardly rume to move in. As we wor a-goin' along we had a rayther smart shower o' rain, and all on a sudden a great glass winder come a-slidin' down right in front o' our faaces, and as I happened to be jest a-bobbin' forrard, it hit my nose and tuke all the skin off the tip. 'Well,' I say to Sairey, 'this is the last time I shall come into one o' these; for a nastier, uglier, ill-conwenienter thing'n this I never seed.'

To the Tower

Here we had to pay a shillin' aach. The fust thing that stammed me wor that somebody that I thowt must be one o' the highest lords in the land, 'cos he wor dressed up so gay and fine, wi' crowns and things about his coat, and beautiful ribbons all over his hat, came up to us and seven or eight more, and sed he wud show us all round the buildin', and explain all the things that wor to be sin. 'Well,' I thowt, 'this is suffin for owd Giles Hobbins to be showed over this graat buildin' and be talked to by a lord. This aloan is worth all the trouble I a-bin put tu to git here.'

Meeting a veteran

Then we weant into a place where there wor thousands upo' thousands o' guns and bayonets, and swords and pistols all shinin' like silver, and put into the most wunnerful forms. While we wor a-gapin' at these, I say, 'My lord, it appear to me by the luke o' this rume, that you are gettin' ready for the Prooshans.' 'Hullo!' he say; 'by George I know that manner o' spaach; yow're a countryman o' mine; yow come from Norfolk.' And he straached out his hand right over the hids o' all the others. He ga' me a rare grip, and he say, 'I'm nor'n of a lord. Fine futhers make fine birds; wan I am stripped o' these ribbons, I'm on'y a common chap like yerself. In fact, I'm an owd weteran , and I a-carried the owd Norfolk flag in many a blaze o' battle.'

Fond farewell

I can't tell ye how I felt wan Sairey weant away wipin' her eyes, and I say to her, 'Doan't fret, gal; as sune as yow git hoam we'll ha' the banns put up, and on Michaelmasday, if all go right, we'll take the faarm and one another tu for better and for wus.'

Mary Mann

HARROWING TALES

Out of a Norfolk countryside littered with derelict farms and overgrown fields, Victorian novelist Mary Mann cultivated superbly-crafted stories packed with acute feeling for rich dialect and ruined lives.

She was determined to show rural misery rather than the more commercially-rooted rustic charm. Her most celebrated chronicles, first published in 1902, are contained in *The Fields of Dulditch*, brutal accounts of blighted labouring families at a time when demeaning poverty was not only commonplace but seemingly inevitable.

A merchant's daughter born in Norwich, she married a local squire in 1871 and moved to the small village of Shropham, near Attleborough, first to Church Farm and then to her husband's family seat at Shropham Manor. Her writing drew heavily on suffering and injustice all around, employing a potent mixture of colourful dialect and bitter humour to underline depths to which parts of Norfolk had sunk.

Stark local voices are at the heart of harrowing tales providing a telling answer to any lingering nostalgic notions about the 'good old days' on the land. In an unpublished foreword to *The Fields of Dulditch*, Mary Mann described that fictional village clearly based on Shropham as 'a depressing neighbourhood, certainly. As I detail its several features I'm appalled at the bleakness, the dreariness of the prospect.'

When these grim stories were republished in 1976, sparking fresh hopes of belated but genuine appreciation of her work, Ronald Blythe, of *Akenfield* fame, said in his introduction; 'Although she reproduces the picturesque speech patterns of this lowly, grimly-rooted and – for her – blighted society with sufficient colour to entertain the reader, her central purpose is not to show rustic charm but rural plight.

'By enduring the misfortune of their birth, their ignorance, their incessant toil and their malnutrition, her characters receive their own special nobility, and it is this which ultimately concerns her. She describes first the barren soil of a particular life and then the little miracle of its flowering.'

She helped teach reading at the village school, organised treats and was a frequent visitor to the labourers' homes. When her husband died in 1913 she took a home at Winterton and finally moved to Sheringham. Her gravestone in Shropham churchyard is an open book with the epitaph; 'We bring our years to an end as it were a tale that is told.'

Mary Mann used Norfolk dialect liberally throughout her work in a way no other writer has matched either in terms of expanse or impact. She didn't call it up just for embellishment or entertainment but placed it at the centre of her savage indictment of an unrelenting battle for survival in the Norfolk countryside.

This story, although a Dulditch one, comes from her volume *Men and Dreams*.

LEVENSES

The first day of harvest. The sun hot upon the field where the reaper is noisily cutting its broad pathway through the corn. The shadow of the hedge and the two great elms by the gate is thrown black upon the stubble. Within the shade a group of women are seated in the tidy white aprons and with the generally cleaned-up appearance exacted by rural custom at the time of year and the hour when the noontide meal is due. Beside them, in the long dry grass of the bank, where the lavender-coloured scabious, the small scarlet poppy, the slender, wiry mouse-ear sway on their long stalks, the baskets are standing which contain the 'levenses' for the workers in the field.

''Tain't on'y a heavy time for th' men.'Tis th' wives as bear th' brunt of it,' one of the women was saying. 'I ha' left my gal, Ireen, to drag th' coach wi' th' little uns and the heaviest o' th' things. She ain't on'y twalve, come Janivary, but she ha' got th' strength o' t'ree o' me.'

'You're lucky as you ha'n't only one man to perwide for, tro' th' harvest, Mrs Drake,' the woman who sat beside her remarked.

'I ain't none so sure,' Mrs Drake made answer. 'If so be as you've got t'ree of 'em, Mis' Browne, you ha' th' wages o' t'ree to dale with, remember. And a matter o' fourteen poun', I reckon, a-comin' in at th' ind of th' harvest,'

'Wait, bor, till yours is growed up like mine – for the boys is as hungry as th' man – and see what they kin ate! – Here come yer Ireen, Mis' Drake, wi' Ronald and th' lessest little boy i' th' cart. Min' th' gate-pos', Ireen,' she screamed, as the child in question appeared on the scene.

'What a keerless little mawther you be!' her mother scolded the newcomer. 'You as near as nothin' tarned th' coach over by the pos'. What for d'ye imitate runnin' when th' two little uns is behind ye?'

Ireen, white-haired, red and round and shining of face, was seen to be excited. 'Bobby Wapple, he ha' fell down i' th' midder, a-bringin' his father's wittles,' she was shouting as she approached, tugging at the long handle of the green-painted go-cart, in which lay two children asleep beneath a bottle, a drinking mug, and a basket of provisions. 'He's a-hollerin' like a good un, and th' drink's spilt inter 'is basket.'

'Well, I never!' the women said in a chorus, and stared, pleasantly stirred, upon Ireen. Some children seated by their mothers scampered to their feet and flew off to the scene of disaster.

'Kin I go back and pick up th' pieces, and help Bobby Wapple?' the little girl asked.

'No, and can't!' the mother promptly announced. 'You stop along o' me, and kape a-jogglin' th' cart wi' the little uns.'

'Theer! The cutter's stopped!' another voice cried. 'Here come th' men. They'll be riddy for a drink, I'll lay my life on't.'

The labourers came, slouching heavily over the golden stubble. They picked up their discarded coats and neck-handkerchiefs from the bank, donning them, or making of them pillows for their heads as they lay down, sprawling beside their wives. One, a neglected-looking man of forty, with a dark and miserable face, a dirty wisp that had once been a neck-tie, and once been scarlet, binding his torn shirt about his gaunt throat, stood for a minute looking over the group.

'Wheer's my Bobby?' he asked.

'He've fell and broke th' bottle into's basket,' Ireen, anxious to deliver the intelligence, panted out.

'Oh!' He spoke with the soured, dejected air of one habituated to, but not resigned to, the buffets of Fortune, and removing himself from the rest, sat down upon the warm grass amid the gently stirring flowers of the bank. There, his face turned in the direction in which Bobby should come, he waited; while the slices of harvest cake, the slices of bread and cheese, the mugs of drink were dealt out to the luckier men.

'Sarve 'm right,' Mrs Drake, with her mouth full, was remarking to Mrs Browne. 'Set a little un o' nine yare old to order his wittles, and to kerry 'em. Why don't the man git a woman to do for 'm and live dacent-like?'

'Tom ha' had enough o' women,' one of the men said. 'Th' one he'd got runned 'm inter debt, and left 'm to help hisself, poor beggar.'

'A matter of eight months ago come the fif' o' September 'tis since Charlotte bust up with 'm and took herself off. A fine time him and Bobby ha' had iver since! And him that proud and shut up he ha'n't niver asked no neighbour to do 'm a hand's tarn.'

One of the younger men got up and carried a mug of beer to him who sat alone. He accepted, and drank it in silence, still looking towards the gate through which Bobby should come.

The child appeared at length, but not alone.

'My word!' said Mrs Drake, staring with all her eyes.

'If that ain't Charlotte, I'm a dead woman!' said Mrs Browne. 'You may bet your life the hussy have come back!'

The woman to whose skirts Bobby Wapple was clinging passed without any recognition the group of old neighbours and acquaintances on the bank. So set were her eyes and thoughts on the lonely figure beyond, it is possible she did not even see them. She stood before him for a minute, and watched his dark, lean face turn yellow beneath the tan. His mouth dropped open, his eyes stared. But he said nothing, and without a word she slipped to the place beside him on the bank. Bobby, with an anxious look at his father, settled down upon the skirt of her dress.

'Wheer's my wittles?' the father demanded of the boy, who began to whimper.

'I bruk th' bottle, daddy. They're spilt.'

'Is they all spilt?'

'Oh, Tom!' the woman said pitifully. 'I looked i' th' basket. There weren't nothin' but dry bread theer.'

''Tis on dry bread him and me ha' lived for a matter of eight months – thanks to you,' the man said. He turned and looked at her with fierce reproach. 'You runned me up bills I thought was paid, to a matter o' fi' pound. Fi' pound! You ruined me; and then you tarned your back, and cut and run; and left him and me to fend for oursel's. And we ha' nigh starved, le' me tell you. A fine mother and wife you be! What are ye a-doin' of here? Who axed ye to come? I swore I'd let my tongue rot out afore I axed ye; and I wull. What are ye a-doin' of?'

'I thought as you and Bobby 'ud be muddled i' th' harvest time. I felt as if I'd got to come and lend a helping hand!' she said, and trembled where she sat.

'I never axed ye?'

'No.' He had a grudging and surly manner, but so miserable a look that she could not but be gentle with him.

'Fi' pound!' he repeated. 'A matter of fi' pound!'

'Theer was the doctor's bill when I was ill i' the winter; and th' bill that hadn't never been paid when our little Gladys was born. That got me behind-hand, Tom, and I cou'n't never catch up agin. And then theer was you on yer club for two months wi' your sprained back, and not so much, by four shillin's a week, comin' in; and you that hard, Tom, I was afeared to tell ye. So, mother she say, 'Lave 'm, and come home'; and I took my Gladys and went. I thought as how you'd come after me, Tom.'

'You might ha' knowed me better,' Tom said. 'I swore as th' tongue should rot i' my mouth ...' He paused, raised the mug to his lips, loudly gulped down the beer.

She looked at him, sideways, as he drank: at his thin, hungry face; his ragged clothes. She lifted the neglected and weeping boy into her lap, and began to cry.

'Tom,' she said, 'I went because I was afraid. But I haven't been happy without you and Bobby. I don't believe as you and him ha' been happy without me.'

He put down the empty mug upon his knee; he looked out at the still uncut expanse of corn; the gold of it grew dim, grew black, was blotted out; the coarse hand he dragged across his wet lip shook.

There was a stir among the group farther down the bank. Ireen had started to bump her go-cart across the meadow to her home; the rest of the children made off to play in the dust of the road, to climb the gate, to hang over the sides of the ditch where the water ran in a tiny stream beneath the tall cresses; the women still sat to talk over their empty baskets; the men slouched off heavily again to their work.

'Tom!' the woman said, and touched Tom Wapple's ragged sleeve. 'The fi' pound is paid off. Me and Bobby well-nigh starved to do it,' he said. 'You kin stop and bring my fourses i' the arternune, if ye like.'

Norfolk-born actress Patience Tomlinson as Mary Mann in the highly-praised one-woman show, 'A Tale that Is Told'.

THEM WITTLES

The reluctance to face toil and sustained exertion is, I am persuaded, one of the most powerful deterrents to those who otherwise would be glad enough to go to 'furrin parts'. 'What's the use o' my goin' to 'Meriky if I got to work as I done here? Whoi, they make you work all day long, folks tell me, same as my father used to work. I mean to say as no man hadn't ought to work like that! Wittles? Oh ah! That ain't all! Yow mind them wittles as you brought me in the basket, time as I was so bad? "Bless the Lord!" ses I, "I'll hev a belly full!" Now you'll hardly credit it, but I laid and cried that night cos I *cudn't*, no I railly *cudn't* swaller it all – I had to wait till next morning – sure as you're a sittin' there. Well, and that's what I'm a thinkin'. What's the use of your hevin' a heap of wittles and you that tired as you ain't no stomach for 'em?'

Augustus Jessopp, *Arcady: For Better For Worse*, 1885

James Blyth

MARSHLAND EDGE

James Blyth was another prolific local novelist to make a bold mark in the field of rural realism – but he stands out as a much more complex and controversial character.

He wrote far too much – he had 25 novels published between 1906 and 1909 – and tried his hand at many styles. However, his strongest work shows a rare flair for the local dialect, not just in humorous interludes but in serious, even tragic passages.

He was born Henry James Clabburn in 1864 at Thorpe St Andrew, educated at Norwich School and Corpus Christi College, Cambridge, and then articled to a firm of solicitors in Lincoln's Inn. Something occurred which caused him to flee London – a doomed romance is the most popular theory – change his name and bury himself in a cottage on the edge of the marshes at Fritton in the south-east corner of Norfolk.

It was fertile country for a 'refugee' forced to make a living from his pen. *Juicy Joe, A Romance of the Norfolk Marshlands*, published in 1902, remains his most original and powerful evocation of rural existence, not just for highlighting extreme contrast between the metropolis and the sparsely-populated marshlands, but for dealing with important contemporary questions such as divorce laws and women's rights.

Even so, Blyth appeared to unravel what many regard as a callous streak in his introduction to *Juicy Joe*, sparing no feelings as he laid into simple folk among whom he had chosen to live:

> The habits, customs and morality have seen no change for centuries; Christianity is used solely as a cloak for vice. The more regular the church or chapel goer, the greater the hypocrite.
>
> Witches, wizards, ghosts and phantom animals are, if the tales

of the marshes are to be credited, as common as mushrooms. To throw any doubt upon the powers of the local witch is to incur the opprobrium and contempt of the whole neighbourhood. It is difficult to believe that such places exist in England in the twentieth century.

Perhaps he kept his distance socially – as befits one who has been properly educated and worked in London – but he clearly tuned in to characters and events around him for a regular supply of raw material. When he was at his most scurrilous, it had to be a blessing that targets of his ire were most unlikely to curl up in bed and sample his latest volume.

It may be a bit simplistic to infer Blyth took advantage of those who inspired much of his writing but the relationship clearly lacked the sort of compassion Mary Mann felt for the struggling families of Dulditch.

Whatever the verdict on Blyth's portrayals of his marshland neighbours, an impressive grasp of local dialect still shines through his best work, including a range of short stories laced with genuine humour.

This is a prime example of Blyth's craft from 1904:

WITH A VIEW TO MATRIMONY

'Can a dew anything moor for ye, Sally?' said Bob Heron, the cowman, to his sister, as he finished banging the mud and 'muck' off the mats against the outhouse wall.

'Why, whatever ha' come to ye?' said his sister, 'D'ye want anything?'

For years Sally had taken upon herself the unenviable task of looking after her old father and of 'mothering' her three younger brothers. Her effort to keep them going in food and clothes were wont to meet with more unmerited abuse and foul language than any return in the shape of attention, gratitude or help. This she felt the more as she was a woman with ideas of refinement that were unusual in the neighbourhood of Frogsthorpe, and took to heart the complaints of her great loutish brothers that 'they hadn't got noo mother'. Bob's desire to assist her in any way surprised her.

'Narthen to sigerfly,' said Bob, sheepishly. 'Can't a dew narthen moor?'

Sally bustled about and deftly tidied up the kitchen. Out of the corner of her eyes she watched Bob hanging round uncomfortably with an evident wish to ask something and a reluctance to make a start.

'Shall a slush the bricks down for ye?' inquired Bob.

'Come on do,' said Sally. 'Tell us what 'tis. Surely to goodness you ain't afeard.'

'Will ye prarmus not to put the grin ontew me?' Bob asked.

'Why should I want to do that for?' said Sally, who was getting inquisitive, and knew the only way to extract information from her brother was to evince no curiosity. 'But just as ye like. I can't keep muddlin' about here all the mornin'.'

'I want ye to tell me what to saay,' Bob gasped out.

'Say? Say what? Whatever are you talkin' about? I don't know the meanin' on't.'

'Well! There's a gal!' Bob began nervously.

'Ah! There's plenty o' them,' said Sally, unconcernedly.

'I want ye to tell me what to saay in a letter,' burst out Bob. 'Lor, Sally! She's a gre't wench! She's bigger'n yew. Har hair's that black! 'Tain't like yarn. (Sally was fair.) She's big as me. An' har eyes! – lor! har eyes fare to goo right trew ye they be se shiny an' se black.'

'A love letter?' said Sally. 'No, Bob; I don't know nothin' about love. I ain't goin' to mix up along o' no love.'

'Noo, noo!' expostulated Bob. ''Tain't come to that yit. But I see har brother t'other daay, an' he axed me to goo oover an' see har, an' I axed him if I should writer an' tell har I wuz a-comin', an' he said as he'd find out.'

'D'ye want to walk out with her, then?' said Sally.

'I doan't knoo azackly as yit,' Bob answered. 'D'ye think she'd maake a good wife?'

'How can I tell?' asked Sally, with some show of reason. 'Do I know her?'

'Noo,' said Bob. 'But she bain't like yew. She's a strappin' wench, an' my missus 'ull ha'e to wark to help to 'arn the grub.'

'Do she wear a fall an' gloves?' asked Sally, slyly, reminiscent of fraternal remonstrances at her own occasional lapses into gentility.

'That she doan't!' said Bob. 'She shan't weer noo fall nor noo gloves.'

'You'll have to treat her different to what you do me,' said Sally, 'or she won't put up wi't.'

'I'll trate her prarper,' Bob promised. 'She shall hev all the grub she can get down har, but she shan't ha'e noo bare nor stout. They doan't do ye a might o' good.'

Bob was an adolescent valetudinarian in his way, and was just then strong on total abstinence.

'I wouldn't write no letter,' said Sally; 'that's dangerous – she might have ye up for breach o' promise.'

'D'ye think soo?' said Bob, who in all ceremonial matters was guided by his sister.

'That 'ould be best – to see her,' said Sally. 'How offen hev ye seed her?'

'I doan't knoo much on har, an' tha'ss a fack,' admitted Bob. 'She's in sarvice out at Chetbridge, an' har brother axed me if I'd like to goo oover.'

'Well, that appears funny to me,' mused Sally, keeping her countenance, but chuckling inwardly. 'What d'ye want to write for?'

'I'm a-gooin' to dew the thing prarper,' Bob explained. 'Not saame's as yew an' yar chap what never came to narthen. I want to hev a prarper onnerstandin' afoor I gits engaged, an' I hain't go noo mother, wuss luck, an' thote as yew'd help me.'

'You get your onnerstandin' talkin',' advised Sally. 'That fare strange to me she should set her brother on to you like that.'

'D'ye think soo?' said Bob, nervously.

'Hev you ever kissed her?' asked Sally, slyly.

'Blaame it, noo!' Bob roared. 'But I should wholly like tew,' he added softly.

'Take her out an' kiss her, then, an' be done wi't,' said Sally, more experienced in wooing. 'But do you mind you bain't sucked in.'

'What d'ye mane?' asked Bob.

'They say as fish-hawkers cry stinkin' fish the loudest,' answered Sally, sententiously, 'An' har brother wholly holler har.'

'D'ye think soo?' stuttered Bob, alarmed at unconsidered possibilities.

'But har eyes maake ye jump, they be se bright. She's the prattiest gal ye ever see. I'll maake ye a bet on't,' he added, by way of self-consolation.

'I spooz,' he said, after a pause – 'I spooz ye 'ouldn't write for me an' ax her if she'd walk out wi' me. I hain't got noo mother to dew it, wuss luck.'

It may be incidentally remarked that Bob was twenty-two years of age, and, with his brothers, was always lamenting the want of a mother. That lady, during her life, left the charge of her young children altogether to Sally, and neglected them and her home equally.

'Yew may take your oath o' that,' answered Sally, firmly, in reply to Bob's hint. 'If ye got sucked in you'd lay it all on to me. You must hoe your own land. You better tell her brother you'll meet her o' Sunday.'

'D'ye think soo?' said Bob; and subsequently acted on her advice.

When Bob had finished the milking on Sunday morning, and arranged for an evening substitute, he grew into a fever of unrest. 'Sally,' he called, 'wheer's my clane shut? Wheer's my collar? Will ye black my bewts for me? I'll gi'e ye tuppence. Come an' tie my tie. Shall a weer a flower? D'ye think she'll like to goo to chapel? How dew a look in my new clothes?'

At last Sally got him off, and turned her attention to the midday dinner.

She sat up for his return at night. He came in about ten, and found his sister alone; the others had gone to bed. His face wore an expression of mingled indignation and shame.

'Well, how did you get on?' said Sally. 'Hev you had your tea?'

'I doan't want noo tea,' said Bob; 'Le'ss go to bed.'

'Good night, then,' said Sally, knowing there was more to come, but making a pretence of turning out the lamp.

'Blaame it,' struck in Bob, hoarsely, 'she an' har brother met me at Chetbridge just as the Swan waz oopenin'. She said she wuz dry, soo I axed her in to hev some'at. T'ree glasses o' stout fer har and t'ree glasses o' aale fer har brother, I paaid foor – tha'ss ninepence – an' a glass o' mild bare fer me is tenpence; and neither o' them offered to paay a farden. Then arterwards Tom left us, an' we walked to St. Mary's-on-the-Fen, an' she said as we wuz travellers, an' walkin' made har wholly dry. Soo we went into the King's Head, an' she had t'ree moor glasses o' stout, and a half o' mild fer me. Tha'ss fivepence-ha'p'ny, and tenpence is one and t'reepence-ha'p'ny. She never paaid fer narthen.'

'Why, Bob bor, you must ha' been a fool!' said Sally, chuckling inwardly. For Bob is notoriously parsimonious.

'D'ye think soo?' he said uneasily. 'Arter that,' he continued, 'we set under the hedge for a bit, an' she axed me to kiss har. Soo a did, but she stunk o' bare soo a didn't think much on't. Then she kep' a-scrowgin' up agin me till she went asleeap. When she woke up we walked to Turlham, an' I axed her if she'd like ta goo to chapel. But she said that wuz past six an' she wuz dry; soo we went into the Queen's Head, an' she had t'ree moor glasses o' stout an' a half o' mild for me. Tha'ss fivepence-ha'p'ny, an one an' t'reppence-ha'p'ny is one an' nine. Gooin' hooam to Chetbridge that wuz gettin' dark; but she wanted to set under the hedge agin. Howsomedever, I said the ground was damp, an' she said as I wuz a sorft fewl, an' we'd best git on to the Swan before they shut. But I'd had enow on't an' come hooam. Tha'ss just like yew, ye … mixin' me up along of a wench what cost me one an' ninepence, an' would ha' done moor if I'd ha' let her. Now's the time when I feeal I hain't got noo mother. I shan't gi'e yew yar shillin' this weeak out o' my money. I must look arter myself same as yew dew; livin' hare, kep' like a queean a-dewin' narthen. Nice dewin's I call it.'

And Bob went up to bed grumbling and cursing while his sister laughed silently downstairs.

Bob is still a bachelor. But he has another girl in his eye, and wants Sally to test her quality before he commits himself to another one-and-ninepence Sunday.

DORZLED!

'Danny be noffen but a stay-where-you–be's and that almighty dorzled (muddle-headed), but Jane be wholly stirren, an' a manager,' old Aaron Pryke said, when an unusually bad attack of 'they mischiefful ould brontics' impressed on him the necessity of making his will.

'But,' he continued, 'Danny do be boy and Jane be gel, and there do have been a Pryke at Mount Pleasant sin' my grandfather's time an' his father afore he.'

Eventually, old 'Master' Pryke left the little white house on the rise just out of Water Middleton to his nephew for life, to go to Jane if Danny died without children. 'And,' wheezed the old man, 'set it down that it be my last wish – and order – that Jane do live at Mount Pleasant wi' her brother, an' that Danny do bide by Jane's say as oft as there be somethen pertic'ler goen orf.'

(Marian Bower, *East Anglian Neighbours*, 1925)

Arthur Patterson

NATURAL NOTIONS

A self-taught naturalist and artist drew memorable scenes in words and pictures of one of our most evocative areas – Breydon Water.

Arthur Henry Patterson (1857 – 1935) became a leading authority on the estuary at Great Yarmouth. It inspired so much of his writing under the delightfully self-effacing pen-name of 'John Knowlittle' as he mixed with colourful characters like Pintail Thomas, Ducker Chambers, Stork Thacker and Short'un Page while they made their living on muddy waters.

He wrote 26 books along with hundreds of articles for newspapers, periodicals, leaflets and reports for natural history organisations. *Wild Fowlers and Poachers*, first published in 1929, was 'my last testament of Breydon – those I knew as a lad ... eelers, smelters, walking gunmen, wild fowlers, and poachers.'

Patterson also made an impressive mark as a dialect writer with a highly individual style and endearing sense of humour as he contributed Melinda Twaddle's Notions on a weekly basis to the *Yarmouth Mercury* from 1893 until 1931, a long-serving record destined to inspire several others towards regular columns for their local newspapers. As with his books, he illustrated his articles with sketches in pen and ink.

Born in a Yarmouth Row, he had a variety of jobs including zookeeper, salesman, relief postman, taxidermist, sewing machine salesman and warehouseman before taking the role of truant officer, a role in which he excelled, winning countless youngsters over with stories of birds and animals. However, it was as a naturalist that he made a reputation still glowing today.

Just a few months before his death, he was elected an Associate of the Linnaean Society of London. Proper recognition at last! Congratulations flooded in, including a letter from the Duchess of Bedford who had put his name forward for the honour in 1906. She wrote: 'It is rather a pity they wait quite so long to give these awards as they would be more appreciated when one is a little younger.'

Patterson haunted Breydon at all hours and was often asked what should be done with the place. He answered invariably: 'Let it alone.'

Here is a flavour from nearly 40 years of Melinda Twaddle's Notions, making it abundantly clear how she enjoyed a style very much her own! They carry a strong topical feel while leading characters in Yarmouth and Gorleston, especially councillors and business folk, probably recognised themselves starring in many of these satirical observations;

DRY WEATHER
(Yarmouth Mercury, June 8, 1918)

I don't know if it'll rain before this gets into print, but if it do, it'll save me a lot of worrit over our garden. Law! What a lot of trubble a garding is when you don't get rain, but gets baked day after day by the sun, till your carrots faint below ground, and the onions all run to drum-stix, and the tater storks lean agin each other. I've hed to stake all my cabbidges to hold 'em up, and tie 3 lettises togither to save 'em from fallin of thirst. It's awkwid for a man to see that every turnip gets its dole of water when you starts sprinkling of 'em, speshally a woman – you gets your skirts all wet walkin threw the ranks, everything fare to want to wipe its face on your dress; you fare to nokk down more 'an you bild up. And pumpin hot weather aint all sugar.

'Mrs C.,' I says, 'can't we inwent suffin to overcum drowt, and labour, and make waterin easy?'

'What's Zach's inwentive mind doin?' she axes, 'I'll see him (she says) and we'll rig up suffin.'

So they gets a 10 fut length of old hose from Mr. Buckerham's, sum wire, and tarry rope and a life-belt, in case of axerdints. Then the fules fastens the hose on the snout of the pump, and begins – she pumpin, Zach bein fireman.

'Lawks?' I says, 'how clever! I'd never thort of it!'

And Zach in his pride swings round, onfortshernately bringin the bizness end of the hose pipe with him, when lo! I gets sich a sowsin it nox me over! Then the crax in the pipe opens up, and it was like a fireworx, jets comin all over everywheer; over Mrs. Mugwump's linen, threw Mrs. Tott's open winder – it was tremenjuss! She fared blind to it, and says as how *clean pump water never hurt nothin,* it was as *good as a bath,* and all that sorter stuff. Onfortshernately the pump went rong, and when she leaves off it wants to go on – it spouted when the hose was pulled off; we plugged the snout, and it over-runned the top, fizzling like pop as we stuft rags and dwiles in, and finally bein desprit, the blissed pump explodes in the belly-part, and now our garding is fludded, and we hev to dive to cut a lettis or cabbidge, and watercress is springing up where the radishes grow'd – what we're to do goodness only knows, for the remmedy is wuss than the disees. I did heer the Cobhom and North Denes lotmenters was goin to run the deeks threw a hose, but we shell hev a fludd if they do. We're expectin the Waterworx peepel to interview our pump – they say it'll be a little gold mine, like parafint pumpin, only we shell hev to bild a reservoir.

SANITARY ITEMS
(*Yarmouth Mercury*, June 9, 1923)

Many Yarmouth peepel is none too clean. I told Mrs. Priddlewell so when I see the refuge layin on the cockade in her Row – Row 159 I think it is.

'That aint my refuge,' says she, 'it belong to harf the Row.'

Theer was a old straw pallyass, 4 over-day skates docks, a broken basket, and a shovel full of mat-shakins, and seven lobster tins.

'Why do peepel hull these things out?' I axes.

'Becos the sweeper'll cum round afore 3 in the afternune,' says she.

'If theer wasn't a sweeper,' says I, 'wheer'd the muck go?'

'Down the cellar, or be birnt in the copper hole,' says she, 'and the Newsants Inspexter man will corrobriate me.'

'Shokkin!' I says. And then I called in Row (I could say the number) the lady in the alley was out; and on the concrete stood a bagger flower and three naked tin loaves! I calls Pattson, and he'll corrobriate that. Why don't Mr Middlington lead a mutiny in the Wash Committy and make bakers put a paper jacket on, or peepel take a cloth for brade? Then this everlastin' mat-shakin. I know Yarmith visitors is disgusted becos the lodgin lady next dore hevvin a grudge noks her mats agin Mrs. So and So's wall next dore (for hevvin HER lodgers!) at 12 reglar, jist under the winder where the cakes and pyes is bein manyfactered. I axes Billy, No. 47½, if theer was any redemption against this.

'Mother,' he says, 'that's not the word; you mean recuperation or reprobation – probably you really mean redress. If so, yes; summinge the party.

MYSTERIOUS PEOPLE
(*Yarmouth Mercury*, June 6, 1925)

Wal, frinds, – Sum folks allers fare a mystery to me. Sum do to you, don't they? Now, theer's Mr. Mcdonel Gripes from – well, noboddy knows wheer. He wornt born here, and as far as you know don't know hisself. He's allers out with both hands in his pocket, and when he draw 'em out you can't say they're clean – allers, but they are soft and supple like a Duke's. How he live nobody could tell you. But he do live or he wouldn't be here. Then theer's Tom Foibles, he's out run his dole, and wish he hadn't. Still, he's allers smoking – not fags, but the best navy cut you ever snift on a damp mornin, and as he go past the Town Hall, or the topper Regent Road, or the Key, folks turn and snift, and say – 'That smells like good terbaccer!' Well, praps he's a adwertisment, who knows? Then take Napoleon Totts, he never fare to do much, and when he do, it amount to nothin. He fare to get trust when others is refuged. He must live on air and loans. He bet on Skyrokket yesterday with a borrered shillin and lost, and says, 'What matters?' I suppose theer'll allus be mystery peepel.

POLITICAL EXCITEMENT
(*Yarmouth Mercury*, October 29, 1927)

Well, frinds, – We've hed a dredful weak in our Ward, Golleston, over the Cownsill Elexion. Mrs. Chittleburgh's bin canvagin dredful – nite and morning. Peepel what never notised her afore clasp her hands like as if she was a angel from sumwheer. She's dropt her hauty ways, and curtsey to the big fry, and 'bow agness' to the small. But she aint like a M.P. candydate, she can't kiss little babes in theer coaches without first wiping theer noses on her handkychieft. She don't tell 'em they'll get free coles, nor cheeper stix, nor nothin, that way, as you may say.

She hev a bed-key to nokk doors with, becos harf Golleston aint either a nokker or a letter-ole, thow millionares can hev 'em. She promise to alter that; she show peepel how to economise in sope sudges – turn up her sleeves and show 'em what for! Jimmy Tugwell is bakin cwts. of rusks, and offer six to every father what hev a vote. It ain't bribery – only adwertisement. All candydates hev theer little subterfugees, and lift their hats, wheer they 'ont look other times. Six peepel set their grey hounds on her last week, thow they say they didn't. They smelt her sleeves, and smelt rabbit – she'd skin one last Monday! Canwidgers never orter skin rabbits, nor fry fish when after wotes. If it's fish, they gets follered by troops of cats.

POEM BY JOHN KNOWLITTLE
(Arthur Patterson)

Another song of another Norfolker

Bor, I never cood arn much money,
No matter how 'ard I try'd;
But never wor short o' dumplins,
Or a good owd eel well fry'd.

Bor, I ha' found owd Norfolk friendly,
An' I married a Norfolk gal,
An' when I cum off o' the marshes,
I've found her a good owd pal.

Law I ha' lived wi' monkeys,
An' worked where the lions roar,
But I longed tu heer t'owd curlews
'Whaup' front o' th' houseboat door.

So I drifted back tu owd Norfolk,
And heer I intend tu 'bide;
For the bards an' t' fishes, an' people
Of Norfolk, air all my pride.

When Broadland is left for Jordan,
And Charon cum over th' styx,
Du delve a deep hole in owd Norfolk
Whose sile wi' my ashes shell mix.

Arthur Patterson wrote and spoke generously about a host of colourful characters who scraped a scant living from shooting and poaching on Breydon Water.

Some of them ended their days at the Fishermen's Hospital in Yarmouth, a collection of 14 cottages each with the privacy of its own front door. Arthur wrote of 'Snicker' Larn:

Snicker could not be cajoled into church. 'Look ere' said he, 'I can't come to goin' in there ... it look to me as if I was hangin' around after suffin'. I can't do it!' Larn was a lovable old fellow. He was humoured, for he was fond of advising his chums who had pains and aches. He eloquently praised his patents for quack nostrums that 'would cure all your scrumatic' ... and other portents as well, if they turned to Snicker, who posed as a semi-physician.

Arthur attended most of the Breydoners' funerals but unavoidably missed that of 'Short-un' Page. On seeing Arthur, 'Stork' Thacker said:

We didn't see you when little old Short-un was put under the daisies yesterday. I s'pose you was too busy. Well, it was a rummin'. We berried him in his poor brother Stevey's grave what was built for two. And just as we was low'rin him inter the syle, theer cum up a voice, solumn and slow – it was his brother's voice an' it says 'Hallo boy Short-un, here you be then. But hev yew brung any bacca long with yer?'

Lilias Rider Haggard

COUNTRY CLASSICS

Two of the most original works in local literature started life in dog-eared and grimy notebooks. They were prepared for publication by Lilias Rider Haggard, youngest daughter of prolific writer and Norfolk radical squire, Sir Henry Rider Haggard.

She inherited his literary talents and her books on the county, *Norfolk Life*, *Norfolk Notebook* and *A Country Scrapbook*, underline the durable quality of her regular articles for the *Eastern Daily Press*. However, those two volumes she shaped from raw material in the 1930s stand high on any list of East Anglian classics... with plenty of authentic dialect to savour.

I Walked By Night is the autobiography of a Norfolk poacher, Frederick Rolfe. His editor described it thus; 'What is written here is born of an old man's loneliness as he sat in a little cottage perched high on a hill, overlooking the Waveney Valley, with no company but his dog.'

The second book fashioned out of rough notes, *The Rabbit Skin Cap*, featured memories of countryman George Baldry as a youth on the border between Norfolk and Suffolk.

Rolfe had taken to scribbling down his reflections in a penny exercise book. This he lent to a farmer and the farmer's wife kept it for Miss Rider Haggard. She noted in her preface: 'I have done but little pruning; most of my work has been arrangement of material so as to make the book a narrative with the incidents in their right places … Also such minor services to the manuscript as punctuation and revision of spelling, although much has been left exactly as he wrote it. To compile this book has been a labour of love, partly because it is so essentially "Norfolk".'

In her preface to the second labour of love, she teased; 'Why is this book called *The Rabbit Skin Cap*? Because if you want to read it as it is meant to be read you must put The Rabbit Skin Cap on your own head just as the hero did before he went adventuring down the long meadow by the river ... '

She pointed out; 'As regards discrepancies in the spelling, readers are asked to remember there is no accepted way of spelling dialect. It is a matter of inflection of the voice and therefore the author's version has often been left as he wrote it.'

In his valuable survey of *East Anglian Literature from Crabbe to Adrian Bell*, published in 1982, Ted Goodwyn picked up on that significant point:

Miss Rider Haggard faced a difficulty common to regional writers, the rendering of the vernacular – of dialect words and phrases, of pronunciation and spelling.

Whatever the peculiarities, the writer's aim is always to retain, as far as possible, sufficient of these to give the sound and feeling of local speech whilst not obscuring the meaning for the general reader. For Lilias Rider Haggard, the difficulty involved the whole of the text.

The two books she edited and shaped are models of how this difficulty may not only be overcome, but turned to advantage through the body and colour of the vernacular.

Although she spent most of her life in the village of Ditchingham, near Bungay, Lilias had travelled with her father in Egypt and South Africa. She was awarded an MBE for nursing services during the first world war. A member of Norfolk County Council from 1949 until 1952, she was elected president of the Norfolk Rural Craftsmen's Guild in 1955. She died in 1968.

I WALKED BY NIGHT

Here are the closing lines of *I Walked By Night*, first published in 1935.

I do not pretend to try and lern the Government there Job, but I do think if the Government made some provision for young folk to get work wen leaven school, we should have a better class of people in the risen generation, than we have today. The young ones of today are to proud to work if they can help it, yet look in the papers and se the hundreds of advertisements for servants. The same with the boys, there are a lot of them here in this town that have left school two or three year, and have never done a Job yet as they cannot get any thing to sute them.

There should be no need for unemployment, in the cuntry there are thousands of acres of land oncultivated for the want of dranage and land laid down that should be growen food for the people. Still I suppose there always was onemployment and always will be, but I don't se that Educating them as should be worken with there hands will mend matters.

With all the riten on these matters it seam as if no one can alter it at the present. There is a sayen goen about that if the Cuntry trubbled more about the pounds and pounds the Government spend on things that don't matter, instead of so much about the pounds and pounds they spend on the things that do, we should all be better off.

I think that they are tryen to lern the common Generation to be wiser and are maken them weaker still, any how look at the crimes of today there seam to be more crime than ever befor. Some people say that it is unemployment that is causing it, but I do not think so, I believe it is more enlightment than any thing else.

Children come into the world to live and it is there birth right. It is said that were God send a child he send a way for him to live, but that does not always happen these days. The reports of some of ower schools tell us that a very large number of the children are onder fed and clothed, that is a big shame to our English name.

I wonder wen will the World settle down again – O God let it be sone.

Well as I have said befor I must bring this book to a close. There is one thing I should like to say and that is that I have never raided a hen Rost with all the bad deeds that I have done. I have always had the idea that game was as much mine as any one elses. Did not God say that he gave all the Beasts and Birds for the use of Man, not the rich alone, and the Green herbs for the Healing of the Nation.

I envy not the Ritch man's lot, nor the Prince his dream. I have took a fair share of the ritch.

I am well over seventy and am waiting for the last Roll Call. If I had my time to come over again I still would be what I have been – A Poacher.

So I remain Gentlemen

The Ex King of the Norfolk Poachers.

THE RABBIT SKIN CAP

This is an extract from *The Rabbit Skin Cap*, first published in 1939.

In most country places the working man and woman stayed in the village they was born in, and was reared according to the family tradition. Many a genius must have come into the world his Father following at the plough's tail and followed in his footsteps, on the same farm. Seeing the sun casting its shadow as it rose in the east going to work, toiling on till it set in the west.

Growing from boyhood, blooming into manhood with his breast full of that spirit and creative instinct with which nature endowed him, but no learning and no chance to go out into the world to better hisself, rooted deep down in the soil, till at last he go feet first the way of all men, only known to have lived by his family and the farmer he worked for.

Meanwhile I wasn't getting on so bad at school and was always for picking up what I could. One play time I was standing looking at the girls knitting cuffs to keep their wrists warm in the coming winter and one look up with a smile and say;

'George, would yew like tew learn tew knit?'

'That I should,' I say, and they soon set me to work showing me how to set my fingers till I gits the knack of twisting the wool round the needle, until the bell rang and it was time to go in, when I kisses 'em for the trouble they had learning me. I soon got the way of it they showing me how at odd times, and knitted myself a scarf for winter, getting the wool from an old crossover which was worn by women at that time.

One night Father asks, 'How I be a-getting on at school, and what have they learnt me, and can I count this way?'

A ha-penny wet and a ha-penny dry
Fourpence ha-penny and a ha-penny by
A ha-penny behind and a ha-penny before
Fourpence ha-penny and a ha-penny more.

'There yew are, boy – count that up then I shall know if you be a-larnin' ought at school.'

I went outside, as I knew where some gravel lay, picked up two small stones, called 'em four farthings, then four big 'uns – called 'em one penny each, that made five pennies, four small ones that made one penny, counted 'em up they made six altogether. Thought if there be six in one half the other must be the same, twice six is twelve, that's a bob. In I go as pleased as punch and Father asks if I has a-counted 'em yet.

'Yes, that I have,' says I.

'Lay yer a penny yew h'aint.'

'I know I hev – that's a bob, that is – give me yer penny.'

'No! No! Boy, you niver laid yer penny down.'

'I won, Father, you knows I have – give us it.'

'I'll be blowed boy, yew've cost me pennies enough and I can see yew ha' been to school long enough for the likes of us. I'll find yew a job afore yew git too much learnin' and start a-runnin' round yer betters all ways, shan't know what to du with yer. I'll have yer at work come spring time else my name's not Happy Jack.'

Frederick Rolfe

Harold Fitch

FITCH FILE

Another Norfolk parson stepped into the dialect spotlight as an authoritative writer and lecturer on the subject during the first half of the 20th century. It was his voice which contributed the 1930 Norfolk record to a series on dialect prepared for the British Drama League.

Charles Harold Fitch, whose grandfather was for many years Vicar of Cromer, was raised in the county and attended Gresham's School in Holt before moving on to study at Jesus College, Cambridge.

After church appointments outside Norfolk he returned in 1915 to take up posts at Marsham, Sheringham and Stiffkey before retiring through ill health in 1942 He died at the age of 64 in 1948. It was while he was Rector of Marsham, near Aylsham, that he developed his passion for dialect.

There is a reason for everything, even for the Norfolk language. We must never think that a dialect is spoken just by some unaccountable whim of those who use it. And our tongue expresses most graphically our character and also the conditions, racial, geographical, historical, which go to make it and in which we and our forbears have been living through the centuries.

Fitch took constant delight in weighing up local characteristics, not least among members of his various congregations over the years:

We are slow in Norfolk. It is true that we are sure, but we 'sure are slow.' We hate changes. The land always keeps about the same, and so does the sea (or at any rate the shore) and what is good enough for such old friends of our race is good enough for us. People come along and try to change things. We 'don't say nawthen'; we just go our own way.

Norfolk people were 'timid wi' strangers' and not disposed to make bosom friends of them right away. 'No, we have to "summer an' winter" 'em fust. But when they have passed the test they are admitted to a comradeship that can never be measured.'

He contributed a highly entertaining article containing many of his favourite anecdotes to the 1934 *Norfolk Annual*, printed and published by the *Norwich Mercury*, sharing the columns with such local luminaries as the county's Lord Lieutenant, Russell Colman, doyen of Norwich writers, R H Mottram, and naturalist Anthony Buxton.

These are examples of Norfolk language and character from the Fitch file used in that feature. It ended with a stirring call to support and sustain this important strand of our local culture:

I hope my friends who have told me these stories will forgive me for thus handing them on; I hope, too, that they may feel that they have helped us to appreciate that rich heritage, our local tongue, the living expression of Norfolk honesty and uprightness, courage and patience, shrewdness and wit, local patriotism and blunt commonsense.

And I would appeal to them and to all others who know and love our speech to preserve not only its pronunciation but its words and expressions too. Up to date we must be, of course, and in being so we must of necessity adopt some of the current phraseology and even pronunciation.

But surely it is not impossible to maintain alongside of these a Norfolk phrasing, a Norfolk pronunciation, springing from a Norfolk character. For – the wise men come from the East.

Bad old days

I as a Churchman rejoice in the passing of the bad old days of dirty, neglected churches and unobserved Holy Days, exemplified in the story of the parish clerk of one hundred years ago who, on giving out the church notices on Easter Day, announced: 'Last Friday were Good Friday. We forgot it. We'll hev it next Friday', and the other clerk who one Sunday requested his rector to preach from the chancel steps on the ground that 'there's an ole guse a-settin' in the pulpit; she ain't due to come off till to-morrer, an' that fare a shame to disturb her.'

Don't panic

After the 1931 earthquake a Norfolk labourer was asked if he felt it, and he scornfully replied, 'No, I didn't … I sleep at the back of the house.' An old lady was telling of her experiences – 'That was terrible, that was; the 'ole house begun to rock an' shake. an' the 'ole bed along with it. My 'ole man, he gor' up an' looked out o' the winder an' I call out, 'John,' I say, 'I believe tha's the end of the world ha' come!' 'Yes, M'ria,' he say, 'I believe that hev – No! tha's all right, them shallots is still there!'

Rough medicine

One farmer met another at Norwich market and complained of the illness of a horse. His friend told him that a horse of his had had the same complaint, and that he had given it a certain medicine from the 'chymist'. The farmer went home, got some of the medicine from his 'chymist' (and how many people know that that is the right way to spell the word?) and gave it to his horse, which thereupon died. The next time the farmer met his so-called friend he complained of the bad advice he had given – 'I give my hoss some o' that there stuff what yew give your's, an' that died!' 'Well, bor, tha's a masterpiece, so did mine!'

Bluntly speaking

The other day I heard of a man who wanted to be 'buried decent', and to that end had had his coffin made some years before it was likely to be needed and kept it in the front room. During a recent illness his clergyman visited him and the patient remarked that all was ready – 'Do yew go an' see that there coffin.' The parson did so (we always do these things) and said to the man's wife what a handsome coffin it was. The reply was, 'Yes, I s'poose tha's all right. But I'll be glad to see the back of it; that dew clutter up the place so.'

Just checking

A Norfolk rector was once visited by an agitated old lady parishioner rather early in the morning. 'I'm sorry to trouble yew at this time o' the morn', Rector, but I thought yew could intarpret a dream I had last night. I dremp' I saw my ole man – yew remember him, don't yer? Well, he come an' stood by my bedside, an' he look beautiful. He had a crown on his hid an' a harp in his hand, an' a long white robe on, oh! he *did* look beautiful. D'yew think that mean rain?'

Country cousin

A Norfolk girl went up to London to service in a big house where there were many other servants who chaffed her for being a 'country cousin'. One day, having been out shopping, she came back and rang the door bell for admittance. The footman who let her in pleasantly remarked, 'Well, here's our country cousin back.' She looked at him and said, 'There now, ain't London a wonderful place; all yew ha' got to do is push a button an' out pop a fule!'

From the rear

In a certain Norfolk town some forty years ago, the Salvation Army band-leader used to march backwards in order to control his band more easily. One day the Salvation Army officer got into a train with a fisherman who began to smoke, a practice which was rebuked by the Salvationist on the ground (inter alia) that if we had been meant to smoke we should have been provided with chimneys in our heads. The fisherman brightly replied, 'Well, bor, that fare to be sense, that du; I hadn't thought o' that. An' that remind me o' suffin' I ha' wanted to ast yew for a long time – Don't yew think that if yar band-leader had bin meant to walk back'ards, the Lord would ha' put his feet hind-sight foremost?'

Puckish wit

I remember talking to a dear old friend of mine, a real rustic, about the old days of our parish, and we reached the subject of his family. I asked him if he had any brothers. 'Yes, one and a half.' Naturally a little puzzled, I asked whether that meant he had a brother and a half-brother. 'No, that don't.' 'Well, then, what du that mean?' said I, lapsing into the vernacular. 'T'ree half-brothers,' chuckled he with satisfaction at a joke well and truly laid.

Slow progress

This story is surely the acme of laconic shrewdness which will take an outsider about a year to understand. A farmer hired a casual labourer to work in his fields, putting him on about 8 am. At noon he went out and saw that he had done next to nothing, so he said, 'Well, bor, yew fare wholly slow; ha' yew ever seen a dodman (snail)?' 'Law, master, o' course I hev; what are yew a'gittin' at?' 'Du yew must ha' met it!'

Little pitfalls
Our Norfolk people have a genius for mispronunciation. The simplest words contain pitfalls. We know of the mawther who announced a visitor to the rector with the words, 'Mr— hev just come to insult yer; he 'ont contain yer a minnit.' And when we come to medical terms we are 'all up at Harwich'. (This telling phrase has, I believe, nothing to do with the town in Essex; it describes rather a 'being harried', just as 'marriage' does 'being married.'). 'They was half an hour a-executin' o' me' said a labourer when speaking of his recent operation. My wife was once deeply sympathised with because of a 'bungalow' (carbuncle) on her face. And a man's broken leg 'fared to moise' because it had 'just been taken out of the Crystal Palace.' How much more easily such an expression comes to the rustic tongue than 'plaster of Paris,' which sounds dangerously foreign!

,

'How much I miss my hosses.'

HORSE POWER

Although he spent 50 years as a blacksmith, Charles Loynes Smith never shod a horse or even made a shoe. Yet dialect poetry he composed in later life expertly captured the full force of big changes on the farming scene as horse power took on a new meaning.

Born in Hethersett in 1880, he was apprenticed to a local coachbuilder at the age of 15. On becoming a blacksmith he followed in the footsteps of his father, from whom he also inherited his Christian names.

During his first year of apprenticeship he received a wage of three shillings (15p) for a 60-hour week. His pay increased each year until on reaching his 19th birthday it had rocketed to eight shillings (40p). Charles was by now capable of making any piece of ironwork for a cart.

He then joined renowned Norwich coachbuilder Charles Thorn at a pound a week but in 1900 succumbed to the lure of London, working there for a firm making everything from omnibuses to bread vans. The pay was good – £2 for a 56-hour week.

He saved £20, sent for his Norfolk girl and got married. All the while the call of his Norfolk roots became stronger. Sadly in 1909 his wife died, leaving him with three young children. Charles went home to Hethersett where had the support of his sister. There he made agricultural machinery until in 1913 he returned to Norwich to work for a firm of constructional engineers.

Moving to another city firm a couple of years later as a general smith, he put to good use all the various skills he had acquired and stayed there for the last 30 years of his working life. On retiring in 1945 he took his contributory pension of ten shillings (50 p) a week.

Retirement was anything but idle. He was elected to Norwich City Council where he sat on the Labour benches and did sterling service with the housing committee in particular when in 1950 new estates on Lakenham and Earlham were being developed.

A man of integrity and high intellect, he was a forceful Methodist preacher and public speaker. Widely read and a lover of poetry, he delighted readers of the local press with weekly writings, both prose and poetry, under the heading of 'A Norfolk Miscellany'.

Charles Loynes Smith died in 1952. His dialect legacy was highlighted by Jonathan Mardle in his 1973 *Broad Norfolk* book when he wrote:

Poets in local government are scarcer than linnets within the Arctic Circle, so verses like Smith's 'The Team-man's Lament' are things to treasure.

This is true sentiment even if it is not great poetry. It is also very good Norfolk, the best I have found in my research for this book. It comes from a man who spoke Norfolk as his native tongue and wrote it from his heart.

Here is that poem much admired by Jonathan Mardle and many other enthusiasts.

A TEAM-MAN'S LAMENT

I arnt agin tractors. Not at all.
They du git over some ground.
No doubt we want more on 'em.
But I du miss my hosses.

You carn't call a tractor good company.
Will that hear ye come inter the yard
An' let ye know tha's pleased to see ye?

That ha' got lugs med o' steel
But du they tahn backards to listen
Ter ivery wahd you say to 'em?
No fear they don't, not them.
That earnt no good sayin' 'Woosh'
Nor yit 'Cubbear' to a tractor.

That hearnt got a nice sorft nose
Like welvet
What snubble up agin yer pocket
Fer a napple or a bit o' sweet.

Why, a hoss is werry near a Christian.
That know Sunday from week-day.
Go you inter the yard a Sunday mornin',
You'll find 'em all layin' down.
They know werry well thass Sunday.

D' you remember them two brown 'uns?
Prince and Captain we naamed 'em.
I was there when they were born,
Exactly a twelvemonth atwin 'em.
I browt 'em up, I brook 'em in
By the side o' thar old mother.

Ah, they *wor* a pair o' hosses,
The best round here for miles,
Lovely ringles all over their coats,
Dapples our old man useter call 'em.
Thar coats were like a bit o' silk.

You carn't curry-comb a tractor
Nor yit you carn't coox it.
If you du that' bahn yer hand
Or else freeze it.

Ah, tractors are all werry well.
They wholly git over some ground.
No doubt we want more on 'em,
But still thass a masterpiece
How much I miss my hosses.

This poem clearly owes much to his years as a Methodist local preacher and some of the outstanding characters he met along the way. It includes a strong indictment of anyone with the temerity to belittle the role of an agricultural labourer, a calling which provided a strong crop of Norfolk countrymen in the pulpit.

OLD GEORGE'S SARMON

I arnt much of a religious chap. That fare a
  proper mix up ter me.
Some on 'em say one thing an' some on 'em say
  another
Till you don't know whu ter believe. Our wicar
  he's a rare nice feller,
He's what they call a Master-er-Arts. He earnt
  none the wuss for that,
But I don't allus know what he's talkin' about.
  Some o' the chapel folks arnt much better,
They ha' got werry respectable now-a-days. We
  had one here th' other Sunday.
He used some master gret long wahds what
  dint mean nothin' tu most on us,
Mind ye, bor, he wornt no fule. But he dint fare
  to *git* nowhere.

The best sarmon iver I recollect I heerd on a
  fourteen acre fild.
Thass werry near fifty year ago. I was ondly a
  boy at the time,
But I remember as if that was yistiddy. We
  were at wark a drillin' o' wheat.
I was a leadin' the old fore hoss an' that wass a
  rainin' good tidily.
Tom say, 'In with a slop, a heavier crop.' But I
  was werry near wet tru.
I said some wahds I owt not to ha' said, Our old

patner George he say to me.
'Jest you moderate yar language.' I say, 'Ha'
you swallerd a dictionary?'
'I know you're a bit of a preacher, but where's
yar religion got you
'You're ondly a lab'rer like the rest on 'em
Gitting yer ten bob a week.'

Old George was a master one for Scripture
Though he never went to school in his life.
He say, 'Harrer, bor, don't be silly bold, An'
don't never say '*ondly* a labourer'.
'I ha' worked on this here fild, wheat,
mangolds, barley and hay
'For werry near forty year, But th' Almighty
He ha' warked on it
'Since the werry beginning of creation, An'
whether you know it or no
'He's warkin' with us ter day. Let us du our job
properly
'Else all His wark'll be wasted, Don't never say
'ondly a labourer,'
'We are all labourers together with God.'

No, I arnt a werry religious chap, But I
remember old George's sarmon
Though thass werry near fifty year ago, An'
that du fare to make a difference.

The Boy John

EVERGREEN LETTERS

A garage proprietor gave the Norfolk dialect a successful MOT test just after the second world war – and then oiled the wheels for rich adventures at the double through years of austerity.

It would have been easy for Sidney Grapes to ration his passion to stage appearances after earning a reputation as a first-class rustic comedian in great demand at local concerts and dinners. After all, he also had a growing business to look after in an area ripe for development.

He chose instead to go for a two-stroke approach with his captivating sense of humour, smoothly combining spoken and written entertainments to leave an inspirational legacy. A whole generation of dialect enthusiasts used his example to keep alive Norfolk's bright spark of individuality.

Sidney launched the second part of his cultural campaign by composing a few homely lines to the *Eastern Daily Press* in the early days of 1946. The Boy John Letters, holding up a mirror to the endearing characters and traditions of village life, continued for a dozen years until his death in 1958. They remain as fresh and inviting as anything sent out before or since to champion the dialect cause.

As his old friend Eric Fowler (Jonathan Mardle of the *EDP*) said prophetically in his preamble to the second collection of letters published in book form: 'It is believed that these two modest publications may not only serve for the temporary amusement of their readers, but become of permanent value. They exemplify the survival, late into the 20th century, of one of the richest dialects in England.'

Indeed, this written work has attracted academic praise at the highest level and added considerable weight to the fight against directing the Norfolk dialect towards the obituary columns yet again. Professor Peter Trudgill, Norwich-born international expert in the field of dialects, described the letters as 'work of not a little genius ... not only are the characterisations and vignettes of village life brilliant and therefore enormously popular, but Sidney Grapes is also a superb writer of the Norfolk dialect.'

Sidney lived all his 70 years in the Broadland village of Potter Heigham, starting work at 15 for his father, a carpenter and builder. A bicycle shop developed into a garage and motor business with the increase in traffic to the Broads and the coast. The unstoppable rise of the holiday trade alerted Sidney even more to the 'old-fashioned' virtues of Norfolk existence.

His letters were written in dialect but never engulfed by it. He understood the language and the people who used it – even if he didn't always lean towards consistency in spelling. His cast list became household names – Boy John, Aunt Agatha, Granfar and the busybody Oul Mrs W—. Much of the humour centred on running feuds between Granfar and his outrageously nosey neighbour.

The scene was well and truly set in the letter introducing Mrs W— in January, 1949: 'She's an ugly woman. Dew yew knows what? We had a willage social a few weeks back an she wun the furst prize for the woman wot could pull the ugliest face – and she wornt even in the competition.'

Early epistles had readers guessing who some of the characters might be – especially Mrs W— and they were full of post-war austerity as rationing and shortages induced heavy sighs. Even so, a truly warming humour culled from the heart of country life, which Sidney knew and cherished, shone through from the start. Letters were cut out and sent to exiles all over the world. They have sold since in their thousands as beacons of authentic Norfolk.

As with his stage routine, Sidney used these letters to emphasise how dangerous it might be to treat the rustic as no more than a buffoon. He would get his audience laughing at him at a local function and then up would go the admonishing finger – 'Now, howld yew hard, tergether!' – and he would proceed to the cream of the joke in which the native invariably triumphed. Now the audience was laughing with him.

Most Boy John Letters ended with Aunt Agatha's latest example of homespun philosophy with a humorous edge just to remind readers how shrewd, deep and amusing country bumpkins can be:

PS – Aunt Agatha, she say – if people think yew're a fewl, keep yer mouth shut, then they wunt know.

Here are two of the letters Sidney Grapes sent to the *Eastern Daily Press*, both giving full rein to Mrs. W—'s foibles and occasional failings:

GRANFAR AT THE FETE

September 9th, 1950

Deer Sar – Yow will be plearsed to know we ha' got trew harvest orlrite, so I can git my second wind now fit for the oul sugar beet agin. We hed a garden feet in our willage, on the Wicar's lorn, an' my hart they meard sum money, nearly a hundred poun. As Granfar say: 'The hull lot on 'em (includen the Wicar) dint look worth five pouns.' We orl lent a hand a gitten things ridy ('cept oul Mrs. W—, an' she never cum nigh nor by).

There wus orl the different storls, an' orl sorts of gearmes – hoop lar, treasure hunt, sticken the tail on the dicker an' bowlen for a pig. Granfar he hed a go at the bowlen, but he meard rather a moderate hand on it. Oul Mrs. W— she hed a go tew, only she chearted; she hed one more borl then she shud a hed, an' wen she hulled har larst borl she hit the chap wot was a picken on up. He warnt werry plearsed.

I hed tew or tree ice crearms. Granfar he hed one tew. Aunt Agatha hed to trim him up a bit arterwards, 'cos yow see he ha' got whiskers.

There wus a bit of a disturbance during the arternoon, that wus like this. There wus a pail o' worter wi' a shillun in the bottom, an' if yow could drop a penny on the shillun, yow could hev it. Oul Mrs. W— was a hevin a go at this, wen sum boys wot were a fulen about gan har a shuv behind. Well bor, she went plump inter that pail o' worter. Granfar wus near by, he helped to pick har up, then blowed if she dint tell him that wus him wot shuved har. My hart he was suffin savige, she mobbed Granfar an' she say to him: 'If yow wus my husbin I'd mix yow up a doose o' pysin.' Granfar say, 'Yis, an' if I wus yar husbin, I'd teark it.'

Aunt Agatha, who wus a helpen on a storl, she cum up an' parted 'em, an' the Wicar's wife took oul Mrs. W— inter the Wicarage, rubbed har down, an' gan har a cup o' tea an' the Wicar got another pail o' worter. They couldn't find the shillun anywhere. Granfar say, 'I know who ha' got that shillun, an' a cup of tea for northin as well, but I aren't a gorn to mention no nearmes.'

Then there wus sum more trouble; the pig got out. He got inter the Wicar's garden, an' fell into a darty oul hole where they put muck an' rubbish, so we hed to warsh him down (we dint teark him inter the Wicarage). Well, we finished orf searme as we allus dew wi' 'kissen in the ring'. Oul Mrs. W— she meard a drive to git Granfar, but the Wicar's wife got Granfar furst. He wus plearsed; he dint want that oul Mrs. W— imitatcn to kiss him. Well fare yer well agin tergerther. – Yars obediently,

THE BOY JOHN.

P.S.– Aunt Agatha, she say, 'Tha's no good a putten yar fut down if yow hearnt got a leg to stan' on.'

WEEDING 'EM OUT AT THE DOCTOR'S

May 14th, 1956.

Deer Sar – Thank yow fer yar kind wishes. I'm a gitten on, but I arn't right right, not yit. I shull heter keep a duen.

Them oul beet are a cummen up sorter patchy. As Granfar say, 'If we'd a hed them warm refreshen rains, wot we useter git in Earpril, them oul beet would ha' bin cut out long afore now.' How many times have I heard our marster say, when we wanted rain, 'Look at that sky over Norridge way, John, thas a rainen like billyo unter their bricks an mortar, an here's my beet a garpen fer some moisture.'

Mrs.W— she come to ours tha tother day, juss for a mardle. My aunt wuss a knitten a garment for har neece's bearby. Mrs. W— say, 'Talking about bearbies, an their mothers, there's an old sayen, *The hand that rock tha creardle rule tha world.* Aunt Agatha say, 'That wuss true years ago. Nowadays, the hand that rock tha creardle is a gitten a half-a-crown an hour – a bearby setter.'

Mrs. W— she hev some money sent har now an agin, from har sister wuss fairly well orf. Well Mrs. W— ask my Aunt Agatha if she'd go along o'har to Norridge to chuse a new custume.

Well that wuss orl a jorb. Yer see Mrs. W- she ha got wide shoulders an she's orl tha way down alike, so she's a werry orkard shearpe to fit.

Well, she got rigged up in the finish. Aunt Agatha say to har, 'Well, what about a new hat fer Whitsun?' Mrs. W— say, 'No, I hev got a new hat.' My Aunt Agatha knew all tha time that Mrs. W— ha got scores o'hats a'toom, wot she bought at rummidge searles, an she's sure ter rig one up out o' that lot wi' flowers an feathers.

Granfar say, 'Oul Mrs. W— never go nowhere a Sundays, but I lay yow a shillun she'll go ter church, an chapel an orl, a Whit-Sunday a showen orf har new rigout an har flower show hat.

Oh, I must tell yer suffen wot happened.

Our Doctor, he's a fine man, he meark yer fear better, if he only come an see yer, an thas afore he gi' yer any medesen.

Now he told my Aunt Agatha this. (He think tha world o' har. She often help him with ould peeple wot arnt well.) Of course, Doctor git fed up wi' these here wimen what go ter his sargery, when in most cearses there earnt really northen tha' matter with 'em.

Well, one mornen Doctor looked inter his waiten rume, an there they set, seven wimen (all his 'reglars'), an one man.

He sed to 'em all, 'Now this mornen I'm a'gorne to give you all a thorough examineartion an see wot really is tha matter wi' tha' hull lot on yer. I'll teark this gentleman first, an yow leardies can be a unloosernen, and gitten fit.'

Well, oul Mrs. W— an har pal shot out right away. Mrs. W— say, 'I dint come here prepared fer no examineartion, neither wi' mi clothes, an yit mi feet.' Har pal say, 'More dint I.'

Well, that fellar hearnt bin in that sargery many minutes afore he gan such a yell. He halered out, 'Oh, Doctor, you're a haatten me, you're a killen me.' You could a herd him down ter tha Crown.

Well, four o' them wimen shot outer that waiten rume an never stopped till they got unter tha' high rood, then they started a duen up what they started unduen.

When the Doctor looked inter his waiten rume, there set just one ould leardy, bolt upright, a holden her medesen bottle. That tarned out, she was stone deaf. Of corse that man what the Doctor called in first, wuss a pal of his, that wuss a put up jorb. Anyhow that worked all right, becos tha Doctor ha' hed werry few 'reglars' leartly.

Well, once agin, fare yer well, tergather. – Yars obediently,

THE BOY JOHN.

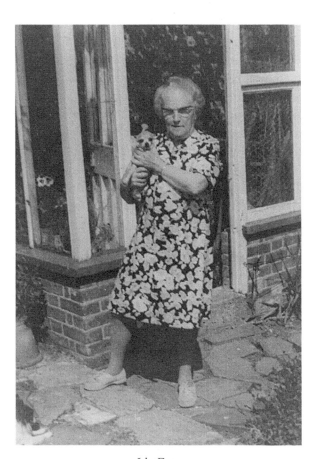

Ida Fenn

FLEGGS FLAVOUR

When I first became hooked on the delights of Norfolk dialect writing I thought Ida Fenn was a made-up name. It sounded too good to be true! But the woman who wove so many colourful yarns out of her rural experiences had no need of a bucolic nom de plume.

She had served her Norfolk apprenticeship by the time she married farm worker Harry Fenn. Ida was born in London in 1899. Her father died when she was a baby and she moved to Weston Longville, a few miles from Norwich, to be raised by her grandparents at Top Farm. Grandfather Walston Goward, mentioned in many of her stories, worked with horses at Weston Hall.

After a spell as a decorator and teaching at the village school, Ida married and during the 1930s her husband was a farm steward at St Faiths. With the outbreak of war the land was requisitioned to become an aerodrome (later Norwich Airport). Ida and Harry lived on farms at Costessey and Winterton before buying Lyngate Farm at Hethersett.

They were completing the deal when Harry died in 1955. Ida decided to carry on running the farm herself and it was from this experience that she was able to write a weekly farming column as well as continuing with her highly popular dialect 'Tales of a Countryman'.

Her most regular contributions were to the *Yarmouth Mercury* where for over 20 years she supplied tales of the boy Jimma and his family. Ida penned many other magazine articles and two novels set in Norfolk, but it is for her tales of the countryman that she is most fondly remembered.

I turn to them when I feel in need of a testing dialect refresher course for Ida wrote in the broad Norfolk of the Fleggs. Much of her writing was done while she farmed at Winterton and a collection of her best village stories was first published in 1973

Warmly recommending the stories, Eric Fowler (Jonathan Mardle of the *EDP*) said:

She has lived the old Norfolk life – and the old Flegg life – and neither radio, TV nor 'foreign' settlers in our villages have changed the dialect she has spoken since childhood.

Moreover, she writes as she speaks, of village life as it was lived in her girlhood. Her characters are true to Norfolk in their nature as well as their dialect. And if some people find the spelling hard to follow, let them be patient with it; for this language, as Mrs Fenn writes it, is about as near to the peculiar sound of Broad Norfolk as you can get by setting it down on paper.

Try this for starters, the opening paragraph of the first chapter of *Tales of a Countryman*. It helps if you read it out loud:

Our parish be like a lot more, there be plenty new housen gorn up ivv'ry deer, but ours, they're like they wore when Faar wooz faast marrit an cam' ter live there. Thart wooz afore I wooz thowt on, well, leastways thass what he tell me.

It carries a rustic lyricism all its own, befitting a special area lying between the sea and the Broads and until comparatively recent years often regarded as a separate province cut off from the rest of Norfolk.

Ida Fenn died in 1980, her place secure in any list of outstanding contributors to Norfolk dialect literature. She waved the flag for the old Fleggs with relish.

These tales first amused readers when they were printed in the *Yarmouth Mercury* in the late 1960s;

JIMMA GETS A BELLY-EERK

'Wuss a matter, owld partner?' my partner Queena seer t'me when we wore a muckin out th' owld sows. 'Dornt ye feer up tew ut this mornin, yow beunt a hullin onnut out zow yow mean bizzness like yow jinnerly dew.'

'I dornt feer werra grand,' I seer.

'Oh. Wuss up?' he seer.

'Ire got a master belly-eerk,' I seer.

'Wuh, why ye bin eertin on?' he seer, 'some of thart new-fangled tinned muck, I spoze.' But I told'm no. Faar wunt ha' nourten like thart in our house. 'I hent had onler breerd an cheese, an a blowter.'

'Haps thart wooz the blowter,' Queena seer, 'thart coont a bin fresh.' Then arter a wild he told me I looked a pore owld thing, jest when I wooz fergitten about ut, what set thart off agin.

'How'd ut strike ye?' he arst.

'How'd ut strike mer?' I seer, 'if yowd a bin up our way this morning at tree o'clock, you'd a knowed how thart struck mer, I set up the garden there, lissenin t' thowld cockrels crowin like billy-o. Thart wornt werra swetta nayther. 'The door dorn fit nowhere, an there's a draft what whistle down the back o' ye neck, nuff t' blow ye hat off yer heerd.

'Pore owld farler,' Queena seer. 'I dorn like t' see ye a sufferin like thart. Yow want t' dew suffen about thart, cause durin the war a lot on'm snuffed ut wi' thart ailment.'

I didn't like t' hear thart, an I felt wuss'n arver.

See the doctor

'Yow barter go see the doctor,' Queena seer.

'What!' I seer, 'Jest f' the belly-eerk. No thart I shornt. He'll nicely git onter me if I go there f' sitch a thing as thart, he onler look arter tham what be neerly deerd.'

'Well,' Queena seer, 'I dornt want t' upset ye, but thaas what yow look like.' I wished he'd sherrup, cause torkin about ut onler meered ut waas, an then I had t' leerve'm in a hurra, an tear off round the bullock yard.

When I got back I told'm if he s'musch as torked about ut any more, I'd hull a forkful o' much over'm. He dint like thart, an he went all sorraful-like an muttert if I wooz a gorn t' be like thart, he wunt talk a-tall.

But leevin off time, I just got m' bike out when off I had t' run. Thowld man narver spuck, onler shook his hid from side t' side thart sooraful.

Besser, she wooz a lookin t' see how thowld sparrers'd bin a pickin off har crocuses when I went up the path an she hult down har fork. 'Cor, booy,' she seer, 'yow look like yower sin a ghost, whatarver be the marter?' So I told'er.

'Go yow in an set down, I'll bring ye a nice cup o'tea,' she seer. A minnut arter she cam in w' the cup. 'Here, drink thart up as hot as ye kin,' she seer. But cor, I'd no sooner got thart down than I wooz off hail f' larther.

'Yow go see the doctor,' Besser seer when I got back, 'Yow'll jest be in time if yow go now.' an bor, I coont stick n' more, an I hopped on m' bike an off I go.

There wooz a greert rume full when I got there. Jiffler's missus set jest in the door, an she muvved up an meered rume f' me. 'Wuss wrong?' she seer, 'thart beunt werra orfen we see yow down here, Jimma, an yow hully look quare.'

I told'er I'd got a master greert belly-eerk. She larft, though I coont see nourthen t' laaf at. 'Thaas what I'm here for,' she seer, a puffin. 'I told Jiffler, I seer the nexter woon yower got t' hev, I're hed nine, but the dowst a bit, here I be agin.' Then lo an behold in cam owld Kenyon, nigh-on doubled up, he wooz. Then I remambert, thart wooz him I heered rustling in the little nex-door hut.

'Whyn't ye harler?' Kenyon seer, 'Thart wunt a bit s'loneler, we mught a set an torked, the time unt a bin s'long. Did ye hear thart gun go off 'bout tree o'clock! Sombrer arter a dinner I reckon,' an he look at Jiffler's missus.

They kep' a comin in, till there got so all the seerts wore took up. A smart gentleman-like farler set nex tew us, an he leerned forrard. 'What's that what you are going t'see the doctor about?' an Kenyon an me nodded, sombrer else said, 'Me tew.' An anourther said 'him an har, an him a-nall,' a noddin at about a dozen.

Pore People

There wore saveril ourthers a lookin down at thar butes, afraid t' own up. The farler looked at his watch, 'I have a train to catch, I suppose none of you would let me take your turn.'

Nobrur spuck.

Then arter a little wild, he seer, 'Funny all this about. Must be an epidemic.' An he looked at his watch agin, an then at the doctor's door. Than he bergun tew sheerk his hid. 'Pore people,' he seer, 'I only hope I shan't be here when you come out, I've already seen one, I don't want to witness another sight like that.'

'Wud you mean,' Freda seer, she'd jest come in arter har Mour's indijestion tablets. He gorrup an cam' over an whispert suffen in har ear, 'Wuh, go yow on!' Freda seer a settin up har eyes. I looked at Kenyon and he looked at me.

Than up got Kenyon, 'I'll be a seein on ye, partner.' he seer an he wooz out o' thart door. I follart, an I see so did nigh on the lot on'm. I biked along, till I suddenly thowt I'd go an see pore owld Aunt Sharlutt, there wornt no sense a gorn hum.

Bor she wooz right glad t'see me an wanted t'know why I wornt at wark, when I told'er, she seer, 'Good thing yow cam t'see me, I'll gi'yow suffen t'cure thart,' an she mixed me up a dose. 'What wooz ut?' I arst a givin har back the glass. 'Rewbub wine, hotted up,' she seer. Cor!

LUCER LOIK THE NEW WICKA!

We're got a new Wicka. Our oldun, he wooz kind a gitten up the tewth, though he wooz a good owld booy but this here new farler, he be as young as the tuther woon wooz owld.

I wooz a trimmin the rubbidge round our farm geert, when he cam' along on his owld bike. 'Mornin!' he seer, and I touched m' cap. I dint know he berlonged tew our parush, dew I'd a stopped what I wooz a dewin on, but I thowt he wooz jest sombry hevvin a gaap about. Then he got off his bike.

He bergun torkin, all about our parush, an thinks I, there beunt much he dornt know. Then he seer, 'You're James, I take it,' 'an I said yiss.

'Well, I'm the new vicar,' he seer, 'an I hope I'll see you in church on Sunday. Also I'm getting up a new Youth Club, Do you belong to any activity?' An I told'm about Lucer, but said he dint mean thart sort of activity, did I belong tew any club. I told 'm Faar had put me in the Wish-me-deerds but he narver kep' up with the payments. So I reckont I dint belong tew anything now.

95

Up the tewth

'No, no,' he seer, 'I don't mean that kind. I mean a meeting of young folks.' But I told'm I didn't know if I c'd claim t' bein woon o' tham, cause I wooz kind o' gitten up the tewth. But he rubbed his chin an looked at me w'out meerkin any reply. I reckon he coont arnser that woon, cause he hopped on his bike arter thart, and hooked off.

When I got down t' Lucer's thart night, Lucer begun chatterin, 'We're had the new Wicka t'see us, hent w' Mour?' an th' owld gal muttert suffen an went on crornshin parpmints.

'He's right a nice young farler, eernt he Mour?' she seer, an thowld gal grunted.

'He set here, in thart there chair what yew be now settin on, an he talked f' right a wild, dint he Mour?'

'Ah,' I seer, 'I thowt thart wooz nice an warm.'

'He wanted t' know if I berlonged tew any social activity, dint he Mour?' I seer, 'Thaas jest what he arst me.'

'What ye talking about?' Lucer seer, gitten all riled up. 'Yow be meerkin a geerm o'me, but thaas the honest trewth, eernt ut, Mour?'

Then I told'er how he'd bin to see me a-nall, and she reckont we wore t' be down t' the Willidge Hall o' Wensdy night, an I wooz t' mind an beheerve m'saalf, cause he wooz sitch a nice young farler, an she rolled har eyes up t' the ceiling an smacked har lips.

New shews on

So there w' wore. Me w' my new shews on, an my red socks. There wooz sarvrel on'm in when we got there, an I wanted t' set in woon o' the back seerts, but no, Lucer reckon she wanted t' go right up the front where she c'd set an look at the Wicka cause he wooz s'nice.

So I tried t' walk quiet, cause I c'd see the Wicka a settin up there on the steerge, but the quieter I tried t' walk the more nize I meered, an squeerk, dint they hully squeerk. Woon o' tham booys at the back harlert, 'Jimma hent paid fer his butes, sar. Lissen at'm squeerkin.' But he only smiled an went on lookin trow his peerpers.

Than arter a wild, Wicka he stood up t' talk, an he reckont he wanted t' meerk this parush a model woon. Sombry harlert out, he wooz tew leert, thart wooz thart a'riddy, w'a couple in clink an half a dozen in orspital.

Wicka, he jest smiled. How he could a' smiled I dornt know. I'd a shut thart lot up if I'd a bin him, interuptin like thart, an I gorrup t'fist'm woon, but thart feered t' set 'm off a lot more, an Lucer grabbed the seert o' my trowsers an told me t' set down an shet m' trap, cause I wooz wass'n they wore. Arter thart Wicka knocked on his teerble wuth a little hammer, an all wooz quiet.

He told us how the larst pleerce he wooz at, there wornt nayther a booy nor gal but what dint belong tew his club, an Lucer set there a gaapin at'm fit t' gobble the pore man up. I jogged intew har an told har thart wooz rude t' stare. Then I heered some scufflin' a-hind us, an a pea hit the back o' my neck.

Suffen a movin

I stood up in m'seert an arst tham if they wanted t' fight, but Lucer jogged inter me an told me t'set down an sherrup, an then I see suffen a movin on the floor. I thowt thart wooz a leaf what'd blowed in. Cor, there must be rare drarft comin trow thart owld door, an Wicka wooz a seerin thart wooz his intenshun t' erect a new parush hall, I said not afore he wanted, fer look how the draft wooz a blowin, but then I stopped.

Thart wornt a leerf, thart wooz a greert owld toad. He wooz a creepin along right onder our seert. Than Lucer see thart, an there wooz more'n woon, there looked t' be about half a dozen, all a creepin about. The gals all clawed up on thar seerts an harlert. Then I see a couple o' booys a tryin t' run off out the door. Cor! I hopped over tham seerts an I had'm jest as they got t' the doorstep. I gan them sitch a lartherin, an than I dragged 'm in an up t' Wicka..

But dew you know, he narver said a waad, jest laafed. He said f'me t' let tham go. He said most little boys got up t' tricks like thart, an thart showed they had spirit, but he thanked me arterwards, an said he'd be hevvin some badges sune, an he look out thart I'd git the faast.

But tham there boys, they keep out o' my way all right now.

Dick Bagnall-Oakeley

ALL-ROUND TALENTS

Richard Percival Bagnall-Oakeley, known simply but so affectionately as Dick to family, friends and countless admirers of his broadcasting flair, was one of Norfolk's most talented and endearing characters of the 20th century. He came to represent the rich flowering of parochial pride and passion in a less frenetic age before the rise of the five-minute celebrity.

He died in 1974 but his star still shines brightly. Any local gathering where wildlife, dialect and humour are on the menu invariably leads to his name, reputation and fund of memorable yarns soaked in the vernacular and laughter.

Thankfully, a few of those stories culled from notes for television appearances and a full appreciation of his gifts and the way he shared them were brought together in a splendid little book compiled by his headmaster at Gresham's School in Holt.

Logie Bruce Lockhart's *A Tribute to a Norfolk Naturalist* describes Dick as 'one of the last true all-rounders, an outstanding if mildly eccentric example of a species of Britain approaching extinction. His joi-de-vivre spilled over, so that everyone else felt better for it. Again and again his pupils and colleagues marvelled that he could excel in so many activities and still find time to be a genius in the classroom.'

Dick spent about half his life at Gresham's as pupil and teacher. He was asked to hold the fort for a fortnight as geography teacher. He accepted the invitation – and stayed for the rest of his career, a kind of benevolent Pied Piper followed around by constant queries, mainly connected with nature, from wide-eyed disciples.

To list Dick's abilities is to risk missing at least half a dozen from the honours board. He translated so many enthusiasms, like conjuring and mimicry, into expertise with consummate ease while his general knowledge was constantly astonishing. If he'd survived to the days of Mastermind, specialist subjects could have included geography (a First at Cambridge), rifle shooting, rowing, photography, ornithology, fishing, art and the Norfolk dialect.

In fact, Dick was bilingual, equally at home with orthodox speech and the broad local tongue, a facility which helped him get on with folk from all walks of life. There was no hint of mockery or patronising as he unleashed a torrent of Norfolk yarns as raconteur, after-dinner speaker, lecturer, teacher and broadcaster.

He represented Norfolk at hockey and athletics as well as rifle shooting. He made himself an authority of migrant birds in north Norfolk and an expert at capturing all wildlife and plant life on film. Dick also served as president of the Norfolk Naturalists' Society and as a member of the council of the Norfolk Naturalists' Trust. Friendship with so many landowners, gamekeepers, foresters and birdwatchers, like Billy Bishop at Cley Marshes, opened up paths to him where the public wasn't admitted.

He collapsed and died at 65 at the wheel of his car while driving to Inverness soon after retirement from Gresham's. He was due to give a lecture on ornithology.

Academic and sporting prowess run free in the Bagnall-Oakeley blood. Dick's grandfather, the Rev William Oakeley, an Oxford Don, married the distinguished archaeologist and coin expert Mary Ellen Bagnall. Dick's father, the Rev Kemeys Bagnall-Oakeley who was Vicar of Hemsby on the Norfolk coast until his death in 1933, was a gifted all-round games player and rowed for Cambridge.

He met Dick's mother through golf. She was an England international. Amy Percival Barwell came from the family of Norwich wine merchants. She was also a fine watercolour artist.

As colourful defender of the Norfolk way of life, especially in dialect and humour, Dick was fully aware of a cussed streak he was happy to share with his fellow natives:

Just as their language, so also the people of Norfolk are tough, resistant and impenetrable. They guard to themselves the secrets of their language and of their humour. Yet humour there is in the Norfolk people, riotous and abundant.

When you read Norfolk tales, remember that they are tales about a highly observant, subtle and recondite people. Therefore always think twice before you laugh at a Norfolk tale – the laugh might be on you!

He also passed on useful advice to newcomers:

One of the first things you should realise is that for lovers of East Anglia, 'Norfolk' is not simply a word that describes a county. 'Norfolk' describes also a language, a humour, and a way of life. For example, we talk about 'speaking Norfolk' in the same way that one might speak about 'speaking Cornish' or 'speaking Geordie.'

Spoken Norfolk has a stout and uniquely resistant quality (although nowadays inroads are being made upon it by television) and only people born in the county are able properly to penetrate it and repeat it with their own tongues.

Actors cannot get their tongues round Norfolk. Professionals who can turn on Irish, Welsh or Somerset with confidence and ease, falter and are tongue-tied when they come to grips with Norfolk.

No change there, then, as television and radio dramas allegedly set in Norfolk continue to give the impression that Nelson's County is wedged somewhere between Devon and Dorset.

Perhaps much-maligned dialect coaches involved in such calumnies should launch a redemption operation by listening to an authentic Norfolk voice relating these two yarns from Dick Bagnall-Oakeley included in *A Tribute to a Norfolk Naturalist*.

A HAIR-RAISING TRIP

Early in the coarse-fishing season I went down to the Sportsman's Arms staithe on Ormesby Broad and there I met old Dan Smith. Old Dan was a well-known local character, always to be found by the waterside, basking in the busy life of the staithe and controlling the letting of the boats. Today he was standing self-consciously by the bus stop, smartly dressed up in his Sunday best.

'Where are you orf to t'day, Dan,' I said, 'all dressed up in yar best Sunday-go-ter-meetin' clothes?' (You'll observe that I always use my native Norfolk speech when addressing a fellow Norfolkman.)

'I'm a garn ter th'horspital,' he replied. 'The ole doctor darn't like the look o'me.'

'How are you a-gorn to git there?' I enquired.

'On the harf arter two-time bus,' Dan observed.

There was still three-quarters of an hour before the bus arrived, so I took Dan into the pub, and there we met one or two other local friends, and spent a happy time over a drink and a chat. So happy in fact that we forgot to watch the clock, and when we next thought about it, the bus had gone.

Dan was 'right concerned' at missing his appointment at the hospital, but one of our friends in the pub offered to give him a lift into Yarmouth to get there in time. He was one of those motorists who always enjoy driving really fast, and soon old Dan, who was more accustomed to boats than fast cars, was embarked on a hair-raising journey, cowering and cringing in fright while the car cut round corners as it dodged and weaved its speedy way down the narrow country lanes to Yarmouth.

As Dan was deposited outside the hospital with two minutes to spare, he expressed his gratitude for the ride thus; 'Well, thank yer werra much young man, but never no more, nor, never no more! I wouldn't ride back along o'you fer a thousand quid! There yar, bor, as we wuz a garn down Cairster causeway, there wuz telegraph poles a'garn past like gravestones in a cemetery. You musta bin gorn a hundred mile an hour. Do you allus drive as fast as that?'

'Oh yes,' came the driver's reply. 'I go a good deal faster when I'm by myself.'

'Cor, blast,' retorted Dan. 'I'm suffin glad I don't ride along o'you when you're by yerself!'

TOP OF THE PROPS

Old Harbert had worked on the farm for at least sixty years. When the grandson of his original employer, after dropping numerous hints, eventually plucked up the courage to suggest that Harbert retired, the old boy thought for a moment and then retorted: 'Well, blast marster, if I hain't thought the job was a permanency I shouldn't never ha' took that on!'

Nonetheless he was persuaded to go. Having worked almost every weekday of his life he found his newly acquired leisure somewhat tedious. One washing day in the springtime he was sitting gazing into the kitchen fire, while his wife busied herself with her washing. But he was seated between the copper and the mangle.

'Harbert bor,' complained his wife, 'Yor in my way. Why don't you goo an' do suffin' useful. Tell yer what, goo you down ter the planten an' git us a couple o'noo linen props. Them there old 'uns aren't no good – time I git ter your end o'the line, your ole combinations'll be a-draggin' their bottom inds across the path.'

So Harbert took his chopper – he'd got his shut-knife in his pocket anyway – and he 'drawed down' to the planten. He selected a couple of good long straight ash poles, and as he'd got plenty of time he skinned them clean with his shut-knife and rounded both ends neatly. Returning in triumph he proudly arranged them beside the back door and announced, 'There yar missus, they're a couple o'booties aren't they?' His wife took one look. 'You silly ole fule,' she complained. 'They aren't no use. You rounded the bottoms so they 'ont hold on ter the ground, and you cut the V orf the top so they 'ont hold the line.'

'W', thas alright missus,' Harbert retorted, and he looked up to the top of his props. 'My heart alive, they're suffin tall,' he thought to himself, and went next door to borrow his neighbour's steps. But even from the full height of these he couldn't reach the top of the poles. So he clambered onto his shed roof, and standing astride the ridge tiles he could just reach their tops.

As he was stretching up to cut a notch in each of them, his neighbour called over the fence, 'Wh' Harbert you ole fule, you didn't want to come round ter mine to borrer my steps to git up onter yor shed roof. Why didn't you use yer skull, bor?

'If you'd took them props round ter the front, you could ha' done 'em outer the bedroom winder!'

Eric Fowler

MARDLE MAGIC

I must declare a strong personal interest when it comes to saluting the work and influence of one of the most able and authoritative writers in the history of local journalism.

Eric Fowler enchanted a wide and devoted readership over 35 years with essays in the *Eastern Daily Press* penned under the pseudonym of Jonathan Mardle. He was an authority on the Norfolk dialect, speaking and writing it with native resource and humour, and also served as a highly-regarded leader writer with the *EDP*, spicing many a dull if important topic with a delightfully crisp turn of phrase.

Encouragement of the vernacular earned him numerous invitations to contribute introductions to various collections published after the second world war. He inspired others to have a go, wrote regularly of the need to keep country dialects alive and generally reigned like a benign father-figure over this comparatively small but vibrant patch on the local literary scene.

His uplifting talk to my Swaffham grammar school sixth form at the start of the 1960s, full of gentle wit and parochial power, told me it might be a good idea to haunt the mean streets of Norfolk as a fearless news reporter. A few years later, when we both worked at *EDP* headquarters in Norwich, we met and gossiped on a regular rota, often slipping into 'squit' mode and exchanging favourite yarns in broad dialect.

On a good day I went out of my way to thank Eric for paving my path to the wonderful world of provincial newspapers. On a bad day I could blame him for another round of relentless chores. He chuckled at either verdict.

Like the bulk of his generation, Eric returned from war to resume a press career with renewed relish. He spent over three years in India before being demobbed in 1946 with the rank of captain. He went on parade as

Jonathan Mardle for 35 years and collections of the essays were published in book form.

Made an MBE in 1968 for services to journalism, he retired from the newspaper staff six years later, an occasion marked by city and county at a unique gathering in Norwich. Leaders of local life paid glowing tribute to his work and reputation at a 'function of honour'. The Wednesday Mardles survived this watershed until his death in 1981.

He had been a close friend and admirer of Sidney Grapes, whose Boy John Letters lit up the *EDP* pages from 1946 until 1958. Eric orchestrated their publication in two best-selling booklets and also contributed his own telling volumes on *Broad Norfolk* in 1949 and 1973. They continue at the heart of the campaign to prove dialect delights still have a place in a hi-tech, high pressure, high tempo era.

Eric admitted his edition of *Broad Norfolk* in 1949 was not the first on the subject. That saw light in 1893 featuring 125 letters sent to the *EDP* and published as a melancholy memorial to the local dialect. More than 400 letters to the paper over half-a-century later proved it was still too soon to write an obituary. A *Broad Norfolk* hat-trick completed in 1973, with the redoubtable Jonathan Mardle leading the attack, reinforced its durability and appeal.

A list of local names for wild birds started that fresh avalanche of dialect in January, 1949. 'People wrote about any and every manifestation of the dialect – and often in the dialect – for the sheer love of it. They clipped out the letters and sent them to relatives all over the British Isles and abroad ... and these in turn sent me dialect letters' enthused the grand compiler in his introduction.

He shunned a suggestion to standardise spelling. 'It is impossible to convey the sound of Norfolk by means of a 26-letter alphabet. It can be done by the use of phonetic symbols such as only philologists would understand – but even then you have lost the intonation, the drawled prolongation of some vowels and clippings of others, and the rise at the end of a sentence, which turns in Suffolk into a sing-song...Each letter-writer has been allowed to spell as he will.'

In his 1973 volume, the ever-industrious Mardle noted:
Today, you can hear as many Midland or London as Norfolk accents on the streets of Norwich, Great Yarmouth, King's Lynn or Thetford. We are told the population of East Anglia is growing –

largely by immigration from other parts of the country –at a faster rate than of any other English region.

And yet the new 'Strangers' seem as interested as the natives in the peculiar dialect of the province in which they have settled, and there is a demand for a third Broad Norfolk, which this book is intended to satisfy.

As a small tribute to all that Mardle magic and as a personal thank you for encouraging me to enter his honourable profession, here are a few extracts from his two outstanding volumes.

BROAD NORFOLK, 1949

The double negative – It is rather surprising that during this most entertaining correspondence there has not been more reference to the use of the word 'nobody' in Norfolk. There are many examples, a good one being that of the old chap who was grumbling because he could not find anyone to lend him a hand with the job he was doing. Not knowing that anyone was within hearing, he was heard to say to himself; 'Tha's the warst o' this here place - there ent nivver nobody nowhere to help nobody wi' narthern.'

Note to teacher – A mother whose boy had been away from school for several days sent a note to the teacher with the following excuse: 'Keptathometogoataterin'.

Piping up – I think it extremely doubtful if the following remark made by a man entering a public-house with an empty pipe and pouch would be understood outside Norfolk; 'Heya got inny bacci onya inni onya?'

Unabridged – Here is a Norfolk man's description of an express train going under a bridge;
'She went shearing down the line, kicking up a dullor. She rushed inter har burrow. Lor, she shruck!'

Taking care – An old carpenter working at a doctor's house was often noticed putting putty in his joints to make a good fit. The doctor said; 'I suppose a piece or two of putty has covered up several of your mistakes, George?' 'Yes, doctor,' replied the carpenter, 'and I bet a flag or two o'grass hev covered up savrul o'yars as well.'

Grave laughter – A story of Windum chachyard. An old man wot worked on a farm at Dykebeck uster take a short cut thru' the chachyard. The other chaps told him he'd be a seein' a ghost but he only larfed at 'em and still kept a comin', five a the mornin', summer and winter.
One of 'em thort he'd play a trick on him, so one mornin when he heerd the old chap a comin' he hopped up onter a tombstone and started a scrabblin away wi' his hands sayin'; 'Lemmee git back, lemmee git back!'
The old man up wi' his stick and cracked him acrorst the skull, sayin', 'Take that, you silly old b—, YOU SHOULDN'T HA' GOT OUT!'

BROAD NORFOLK, 1973

Emphatic word – The word 'wholly' is important in the Norfolk vocabulary. It is used for emphasis. For instance, the weather can be 'wholly hot' or 'wholly cold.'An angry man is 'wholly riled', and a frightened one is 'wholly scared'. 'Fare' is also important. A bullock that fails to put on flesh, or a human invalid who is slow to recover, ' dorn't fare to moise'(improve) and on a 'daggly' (damp) day it 'fare to mizzle' (drizzle). A man who feels out of sorts will tell you he 'dorn't fare noo matters', also 'he dorn't feel wery fierce.'

Harvest past – There is no more need for boys proudly to take charge of wagons in the harvest fields and 'haller howdjee' to the horses. There are no more 'shoofs' (sheaves) to be adroitly bound with a bond of twisted straws and set up in 'shocks'; no more reapers to form a circle round a stranger and, taking their time from the leader, 'haller largees' – that is, shout 'largesse', for a tip. No doubt we should be glad to be rid of the poverty that gave rise to such a custom.

One for all –'Together' is another of our favourite words. Even when we are addressing only one other person, it is still 'together'. Which was once a great embarrassment to a highly respectable and virtuous London girl, when for the first time she spent a weekend at the home of her

Norfolk fiancé. His parents made her very welcome and she slept soundly in a pretty little bedroom on the far side of the house from the young man. Imagine her astonishment when, on coming down to breakfast the following morning, she was greeted by her prospective father-in-law (a chapel deacon) with; 'Well, my dear, did ye sleep well, together?'

Taking a walk – A parson was surprised to meet in a narrow lane one of his smallest Sunday school children, driving a large cow. Shrinking nervously in to the hedge, he said: 'Good morning, Mary. May I ask where you are going with that enormous animal?' 'Please, sir,' replied Mary, 'I'm a-taakin' old Buttercup to be bulled.' 'Dear me' said the parson, very shocked. 'But couldn't your father do that?'
'Ooh, no sir!' said Mary, equally shocked. 'That must be a bull.'

Just be careful – The Norfolk use of metaphor is vivid and often wounding. It is particularly unwise, in this county, to hold forth on a subject of which you know nothing, because if your audience do not tell you to your face that you are 'talking squit', they will remark as soon as you have gone that 'He dorn't know no more about that than a crow do about a Sunday.'

Neither must you thrust yourself too hurriedly into Norfolk affairs, or you will be 'too eager, like Farmer Cubitt's calf as trotted t'ree mile to suck a bull.'

Made in Norfolk – There are many other words and phrases that mark us as Norfolk, wherever we are in the world. For instance, I was once walking with a friend in Sussex when it came on to rain. I made for a clump of trees and said, 'Come on, let's stand up out of the rain.' My friend looked at me in astonishment. Nowhere except in East Anglia do people 'stand up out of the rain'.

Cyril Jolly

JOLLY GOOD!

Gently spoken and carrying a scholarly air, Cyril Jolly seemed an unlikely candidate to add rousing hymns of praise to the Norfolk dialect cause. However, the best-selling author and long-serving preacher played an important role with streams of verses and letters flowing from a prolific pen.

He died at the age of 83 in 1994, when wartime exploits vied with his reputation as outstanding author and dialect champion. Cyril was one of the best-informed non-commissioned officers of the second world war, nursing a D-Day secret which in the wrong hands could have changed history.

Then Flight Sergeant Jolly, he was personal clerk to the Air Commander-in-chief, Air Chief Marshal Sir Trafford Leigh-Mallory and knew full details of the RAF's invasion plans.

After the war, he and wife Hilda moved to Gressenhall, near East Dereham, and it was from this village base that he played a leading part on the local Methodist circuit and embarked on a successful writing career while holding down various jobs, including manager of the Dereham Foundry and director of the Mid-Norfolk Farm Supply Company.

His book *The Vengeance of Private Pooley* told the true story of how two soldiers, one of them from Dereham, escaped the massacre of 97 of their comrades by the SS in France. It was made into a film, serialised by the *London Evening Standard* and translated into several languages.

Other works included *Henry Blogg of Cromer*, the definitive biography of one of Britain's most famous lifeboatmen and still selling well as a stirring tribute to a brave but modest man of the sea. Such was Blogg's reticence to talk about his long and illustrious career that most who knew him were amazed anyone could produce such a perceptive and wide-ranging chronicle.

Cyril Jolly's dialect delights reached a peak with dialect letters to his local weekly newspaper 'just up the rood', the *Dereham and Fakenham Times*, and to a national publication, *The Methodist Recorder*, in London. He started this exercise in 1965 and *Jimma's Mathodist Latters* from 'midway atween Gressinall an' Longum' have a strong touch of The Boy John about them. Many years as a Methodist preacher presented him with a rich fund of ready material from pew and pulpit.

He published a collection of verses in 1978, *A' Leanin' on the Gearte*, including poems by his brother Leslie, written while he was a prisoner-of-war in Java. Leslie penned several others which were buried by his friends in tinfoil from tea chests to hide them from Japanese guards. On his release, he discovered most of these poems had been eaten by white ants. Surviving verses shared the Jolly spotlight in 1978, two years after Leslie's death.

Cyril found space for a few of his own 'serious' poems, like 'Leaving For France', 'Easter Sunday Evening, 1940', but a puckish sense of humour laced with dialect, allied to strong Christian beliefs and love of his native county dominated most pages.

From JIMMA'S MATHODIST LATTERS

Carols at Longham (To the *Dereham and Fakenham Times*, December, 1965)

Dear Sar – I thort yow an' your reeders moit like tu know how we got on wi' our Carel Sarvis on Sunday at Longum Mathodis Charch. Well, thet wus a verra dark nite but none o' thet mucky oul fog an' a lotta fook tarned up from orl round the Deerum Sarcut. We wus verra plearsed t' see our minasters wi' there good lairdies.

Everabodda looked smart 'cept owl Gorge. He kept his red chooker on tu hide his datty neck so none o' those posh townies knew any different, but he hully swet.

There wus a bloke from Mattashull in the cheer – o'corse he wus in the pulput reerly but thass how they tarm it. Then there wus a lairdy from Gressinall arorin' away on the oul organ.

The Sarcut yung people sung tew or tree carels, an' then we orl had a mow in. An' one yung fella sung a solo. He hollered fer ten minits orl on his own. Thet wus orlrite, but lor, wot a hullah! I wished I cud git him onto my garden when the oul sparrers are arter my yung letusses. He'd put the wind up on 'em.

An' then sum o' them smart mawthers from Deerum read sum bits o' vars. Thet maird a lump cum inter my throot so as I thort I hed swollered the peppamint wot I wus a suckin'.

They spoiled things a bit by hevin' a colleckshun. I hent cum prepeared fer that, as they corled it a 'spechul sarvis' an' there's nuthin' speshul in hevin' a colleckshun at a Mathodis sarvis. I wus in a puckaterry. I hed a cuple o' washers orf the oul tractor in my pocket so I plopped them in. I jist hope I sharnt wont 'em this here week, if so I shall hev ter arsk the minaster fer 'em back.

Well, I shall hatter leave yer now tergether ter shut up my oul hins as there's sum tew-legged foxes about, bein' so near Christmas. – Yours verra trewly,

JIMMA.

Garden Feartes (To the *Methodist Recorder*, July, 1972)

Deer Sar – We're in the middle o' hay cartin' an' the garden feartes, an' we've jist hed a big du on our Deerum Sarcut. The wather must hev bin lyin' in weart fer us, cors jist as the invited leardy wus about tu declare the fearte open thet started tu rearn. Mearbe the heavins thowt they wus supposed tu open tu! Anyway thass wot they did, an' they didn't shut agin until arter the good fook hed swum hoom.

Thass a good job we hed a big schule tu go into, but the wark o'cartin' the stalls an' stuff inside outer the flood wus like the days o' Noah, but his animels went in tu by tu, we went in a gret stampedin' hard. An' if his creatures kicked up as much dullah as we did it would hev mearde him fling hisself overboard.

Howsumnever, it wus done, an' the buyin' an hagglin' started. I bought a tin o' soup, I dunno what for, but it'll come in – if only fer boot polish. The teas went well, but du yow know, they charged foar o' these new pence fer a cup o' tea. Thass tu du wi' this here inflearshun.

A leardy sear tu me, 'Will yow estimearte the weart o' this here cearke.' (estimearte sound better than guess). But I dint know what tu du since I could no more estimearte the cearke than our oul tractor. If I won thet would hev bin luck an' not judgement, so where does skill come in an' gamblin' end? Thass the wust o' hevin' a tender conshence – it's wuss than tender fearte.

Oul Gorge wus there. He'd bin dyke-hullin' all the weark an' he jist sat about like a broody hin, moanin' about the rearn. Still it wus a good du, an' I reckon these feartes git pearple warkin' tergather, an' talkin' – if it's only searin' nasty things about the wather.

We're goin' tu hev the dry sports another day – we've hed the water sports.

Yars trewly,
JIMMA

From A'LEANIN' ON THE GEARTE

A Furrerd Field

How dull the countryside in winter;
Wi' dykes full, hidges an' woods dark brown.
Trees are stripped bare an' the medders drab.
But then, thet earnt no better in town.

Yit a sight thet allus warms my heart,
Is a field where the oul plough's jist been;
The arth's new-tarned, neat row over row,
An' the furrers bear a polished sheen.

If the sun brearks through, however weark,
Light strikes fresh arth, a-mearkin' it gleam,
Then I think o' horsemen wi' spears ashine,
Jist like a proud army in a dream.

Thet gleam's the partnership o' sarvice –
Fair exchearnge; givin' an' tearkin';
Rust removed; coulter an' share worn bright –
A pearment fer the soil's fresh brearkin'.

There's a sim'lar partnership in LIFE –
When fer others the hard arth's broken,
The shine o' sarvice catches the sun;
Thet gleam is God's smile, an' His token.

The Onion's Lament

A smelly little onion sat aside his Mamma's knee,
An' gearzin' intu har eyes, sed untu har sed he,
'Oh, Mammy dear, plearse tell me, why should it be thet I
Am born tu be an onion an' mearke poor pearple cry?'

The mother gearzed at har offspring. Har eyes grew big an' wide.
She touched the smelly little brat wi' a parent's tender pride.
'Oh, Ailsa dear,' she muttered, 'mayhaps it du seem cruel,
But if it wornt fer the likes o' us – there'd be no onion gruel!'

Hay hay!

They tell me thet hay is werra scarce,
Mearkin' a pound fer a little bale.
'Cors we know last spring wus hully wet,
Yit all the searme thass a sorra tale.

Thet jist go tu show wot I've allus said,
An' tu me thass true beyond doubt,
If yow mearke spare when yow've got plenta,
Yow'll allus hev some when yow run out.

The Singing Postman

POST IMPRESSIONS

Allan Smethurst's contribution to the Norfolk cause continues to divide opinion sharply. Some dismiss him as a mere reinforcer of the yokel stereotype shuffling across a pantomime stage built on national misconceptions and rosy nostalgia. Others prefer to insist his life and work add up to an important chapter in our local history, a chapter that may be worthy of attention well beyond the county boundaries.

His colourful if ultimately doomed round as the Singing Postman reached a brief peak in the mid-1960s when his catchy anthem 'Hev Yew Gotta Loight, Boy?' placed him on an unlikely pop pedestal, selling more records in East Anglia than all the leading groups... including the Beatles and Rolling Stones.

There was even talk of a trip to America organised by Dick James, music publisher to the Beatles, who announced; 'I believe the sales of Singing Postman records have only stirred the fringe of the buying potential.' The man himself had very obvious reservations; 'I wunt mind gorn tew America ter sing an' strum an' that. For a week, mind. Not longer.'

A shy, bespectacled, buck-toothed performer sampled such national television delights as Top of the Pops and Sunday Night at the London Palladium as well as a bill-topping session on Great Yarmouth's Golden Mile. As a young newspaper reporter working in the town at the time, I recall that summer season at the Windmill Theatre being cut short by illness brought on by stage fright and excessive drinking.

It was clear to anyone dropping into his dressing room during that brief June run in 1965 how life at the top would soon turn sour. Stories of erratic antics fuelled by drink and fear of performing spread with a dreadful predictability after that heady flirtation with the charts. He spent much of the rest of his life as a virtual recluse in a Salvation Army hostel in Grimsby, where he died just before Christmas in 2000.

He worried constantly that he'd be remembered for just the one song despite a crop of other ditties, deceptively simple but crammed with potent images of a Norfolk rural life fast disappearing as he wrote and sang about it. Those winsome, wistful and witty compositions deserve to be shared as slices of cherished local life wrapped in the endearing delights of the Norfolk dialect.

The Singing Postman did not fit into any obvious entertainment niche and most of the national media took the easy way out when forced to take notice and cast him as a harmless little novelty turn from the sticks. (I suspect Norfolk turkey tycoon Bernard Matthews attracted similar sentiments when he launched his successful 'bootiful' television advertising campaign – although he had far more self-confidence, power and money than the Singing Postman).

Unpretentious and gently amusing songs about homely characters and places delivered with the minimum of musical fuss were bound to stand out in the Swinging Sixties. We realise now that Allan's writing talents sprang from far deeper wells than any desire or ability to perform on stage. He was different, as vulnerable as the Norfolk scene he portrayed. His soft, melancholy nature was bound to leave him cruelly exposed before long.

Fame overwhelmed him and sent a touch of self-loathing to the surface. That's probably why he drank so much, to escape the fact he couldn't handle the stage on which fate had landed him. Family, friends and those closely involved in his career must have tried to keep him aware of how much further he might go. And that was liable to scare him even more.

Considering all the weaknesses, I think he did remarkably well to leave so much worthwhile material. Perhaps a good strong woman might have sorted him out. Sadly, he was hardly the type to meet one and confined himself to singing about his ideals instead. Take a bow, Molly Windley, Edna the Barmaid, the Milk Gal and My Little Miss from Diss. Any one of those mawthers could have changed the Singing Postman into a first-class male.

Many of his lyrics stand comfortably as telling verses from a poet of the everyday. He wanted to be taken seriously as a writer, working overtime to find the appropriate image to suit the mood as he jotted down another line on the back of a crumpled cigarette packet. He pulled subjects out of his fertile memory bank, especially from childhood days along the North Norfolk coast, but shrewd and amusing reflections on current topics such as the decline of the quality of bread, mark him as an effective commentator on life's changes and challenges.

His ability to combine sideways humour with dialect treats and simple themes to produce a fresh light on familiar scenes reaches a peak for many in 'Come Along O' Me'. For example, *Aeroplanes go along o'noffin* is a dazzling truth waiting to land while *There's ole boy Hinry orl alone tergether* is pure Norfolk gold.

I have watched audiences of all ages over many years fall under the spell of his songs and sentiments at harvest suppers, village concerts and family reunions. They will continue to inspire as well as provoke nostalgic sighs at sessions of proper home-made entertainment. Yes, 'Hev Yew Gotta Loight, Boy?' will survive as a signature tune that took the Norfolk sound to places it had never been before, informing those who wanted to listen that the Singing Postman's home is not wedged somewhere between Devon and Dorset. However, Allan Smethurst warrants a bigger tribute than that.

He saluted one era and then fell victim to another as glaring personal frailties chased him from the spotlight. For all those weaknesses, and the bitter disappointment they carried, he left a rich legacy of lamentation for a time and a place where he felt people and what they did and felt really mattered.

Here are the words to a couple of his best compositions still going strong and an intriguing monologue he wrote to mark The Great Train Robbery of 1963. Hardly a subject for humour – but Allan gave it his own whimsical treatment to add an extra dimension to what had become one of the biggest news stories of the time.

HEV YEW GOTTA LOIGHT, BOY?

I had a gal, a rare nice gal, down in Wroxham way
She were whooly nice ter me in the ole school days.
She would smile all the while, but Daddy dint know all

What she used ter say ter me behind the garden wall.
'Hev yew gotta loight, boy? hev yew gotta loight?'
Molly Windley, she smook like a chimley,
But she's my little nicoteen gal.

Then one day, she went away, I dunt see har no more,
Till by chance, I see har down along th' Mundesley shore.
She wuz there, twice as fair, would she now be trew?
So when she see me passin' by she say 'I'm glad thass yew,
Hev yew gotta loight, boy? hev yew gotta loight?'
Molly Windley, she smook like a chimley,
But she's my little nicoteen gal.

Now yew'll see har an' me never more t'part,
We would wander hand in hand tergether in the dark.
Then one night I held har tight in th'ole back yard,
But when I tried ter hold har close, she say 'Now hold yew hard!
Hev yew gotta loight, boy? hev yew gotta loight?'
Molly Windley, she smook like a chimley,
But she's my little nicoteen gal.

By and by we decide on th' weddin' day,
So we toddle orff ter chatch ter hear the preacher say:
'Do you now tearke this vow ter honour all the time?'
Afore I had th'chance ter stop har, she begin ter pine:
'Hev yew gotta loight, boy? hev yew gotta loight?'
Molly Windley, she smook like a chimley,
But she's my little nicoteen gal.

Now the doctor tell me a Daddy I will be,
So when I arsk him 'Woss th' score?' he say 'There's only three'
So, here I go, cheerio, ter see how she do fare,

I know what she will say ter me as soon as I git there:
'Hev yew gotta loight, boy? hev yew gotta loight?'
Molly Windley, she smook like a chimley,
But she's my little nicoteen gal.

COME ALONG O' ME

Trains they go along o' train lines,
Cars they go along the rood,
Th'ole self-binder go along o' corn
The poacher he go along o' wood,
Aeroplanes go along o' noffin',
Ships they go along the sea,
An' I keep a'tellin' my little ole mawther
She'll hatter come along o' me.

How yew getting' on?

Now the dorgs they go along o' meat bones,
Cows they go along o' grass,
There's ole boy Hinry orl alone tergether,
Gorn arter cockles on th' marsh,
Little boys go along o' bads' nests,
Climbin' arter conkers up a tree,
An' I keep a'tellin' my little ole mawther
She'll hatter come along o' me.

Wha' yer on hol'day?

Now the morths they go along the oil lamp,
Farmhoss go along the plough,

A rare lot o' people go along ter chach,
An' the clock go along o'now,
Uncle Bob go along ter Bodham,
The ole hare go along the lea,
An' I keep a'tellin' my little ole mawther
She'll hatter come along o' me.

Come yew on.....

Now th' crab boats go along th' seashore.
Dew they go along the wall,
Salvation Army go along the prom.
Ev'rybody go along an' all.
Evrathin' go along o' suffin,
All these things hatter be,
If a noice pint o' beer go along o' anythin'
Yew'll hatter come along o' me.

Cheeeeeeeeeerio!

THE GREAT TRAIN ROBBERY

So old Charlie, he say to me, he say, they're still on about that big train robbery you know. Yis, I say, and tha's a lot a squit. So he say, how do yer mean tha's a lot of squit? Well, I say, all that money wass vallalas for a start. So, he say, how do yer mean that wass vallalas, won't worth narthin'? Well, I say, they wass goin' to burn it, I say, thay wass goin' to take it to one of these here incinerators and they wass goin' to burn it. So, he say, wass that gotta do with it?

Course tha's just like old Charlie, he ask yer a question. Yer tell 'im and he say wass that gotta do with it. Well, I say, tha's gotta lot a do with it. I say, if yer had suffun what yer considered valable, I say, yer won't burn it. Yer won't hull it on the fire. No tha' I won't, he say. Well no more would

I, I say. Well, he say, vallalas or no, he say, they got the hul pleese force out arter it. Oh! I say, wass the idea a that? Well, he say, Thay want all that money back agin of course. What, I say, arter they wass gorn' ter burn it? Yis, he say. Well, I say tha's a rumin state of affairs, first they wass goin' to burn it, they were agoin despose if it, and now they want all that back? Of course, he say. Well, I say, if they really want tha' money back, I say I know how a git it back. Oh, he say, so yer think yerself a rear lot clevra than what they are. Well, I say, I'm clevver enough. Well, he say, how do yer propose to git all this here money back? Well, I say, let the robbers keep the money. Well, he say, how's tha' goin' git the money back if yer let em keep it? Well, I say, if yer let 'em keep it, the first thin' they'll do, they'll go to a bank, open a bankin' account, and tha's 'ow they'll git tha' money back. Oh, he say, they won't do that.

Well, I say, that strikes me as thou' they don't know whether they want tha' money back or no, I say. Well, he say, yer can't give two and a 'alf million pound away like that. Well, I say, they int got it to give away, so 'ow can they give it away? Well, he say, yer don't understand heconomics, he say. Well, I say, you don't call tha' heconomical, burning two and 'alf million pound, I say, tha' int being heconomical. No, he say, tha' int what I mean, he say. He say, you hav' to have heconomics do you git inflation. Oh, I say, I didn't know we're talking about bicycle tyres. No, he say, that int the kind of inflation I mean, he say. He say, yer, yer can't do things like that he say. Yer har'a have gold, he say, that's the gold that covers it. He say, if yer int got the gold to cover this here money, he say, that's vallalas.

Well, I say, yer silly old fool, tha's what I say in the first place, and yer laugh. Oh ... tha's different, he say, 'course tha's another one of Charlie's favourite saying tha's different, mind you, old Charlie, he say, do there caught some of 'em. Yis, I say, do yer know what ther' got. 30 odd years. Blast, he say, tha'll take em a long time do that. Yis, I say, but some of 'em hav' escaped already. Yis, he say, tha' din't take them long to do tha'.

John Kett

TOP OF THE CLASS

A proud surname soaked in Norfolk history may well have sparked both rhyme and reason for John Kett to carve out a reputation as the county's most successful dialect poet – but he had a little help from north of the border.

His wife Mary hailed from Scotland and introduced him to the enduring talents of Robert Burns. That in turn inspired early attempts at writing Norfolk verse in the 1950s as John settled into a long and distinguished career as a village school headmaster.

'Norfolk has a much more limited vocabulary than the Scots and our vowel sounds always present problems. But I aimed at something more serious than the usual harvest horkey humour,' said the teacher who delighted reflective readers and animated audiences for over half a century.

He gloried in his deep local roots and a masterly touch for a precious vernacular in verse. Warmly encouraged by fellow dialect champions Dick Bagnall-Oakeley (another uplifting schoolmaster) and Eric Fowler, he tied up rhythm, intonation and turn of phrase in ways never seen or heard before.

Four volumes of Norfolk delights underlined clear success in lifting his subject matter well above the country yokel and 'bit if a larf' level. *Tha's a Rum' un, Bor, Tha's a Rum'un Tew, Wotcher Bor!* and *A Year Go By* netted total sales of about 30,000 – remarkable figures for poetic offerings, not least those carrying a quaint brogue supposed to be dying out fast.

His first book of orthodox poetry, *Remembered in Rhyme*, was published in 1966 as a thanksgiving for the recovery of his wife from serious illness. Another collection spanning the creative years and including a surprisingly wide variety of more 'serious' subjects arrived in 1997 to mark John's 80th birthday and telling contribution to our cultural scene. *A Late Lark Singing* celebrated a deep love of nature and an unshakeable Christian faith along with that legendary dialect flair.

The doyen of Norfolk verse died at the age of 93 just before Christmas in 2010. Born at Wereham in the west of the county, he went to school in Stoke Ferry and Downham. He taught at Shipdham either side of war service and then became headmaster at Holme-next-sea (1948-52) and Cawston (1952-78).

On hearing of his graduation to The Great Mardling Classroom in the Sky, my thoughts turned immediately to when we shared a historic local milestone over 30 years earlier. BBC Radio Norfolk's first full day of broadcasting on Friday, September 12th, 1980, saw me in harness with Rob Bonnet to present the Lunchtime Programme. (The Dinnertime Show tag came a bit later when indigenous forces turned up the volume.) I lined up John Kett as a trailblazing authentic Norfolk voice to give our initial output the right kind of flavour.

He filled that bill admirably with homespun verses and amusing reflections on his years as a village headmaster. He stressed it was never intended that his dialect verses should be browsed over in silence; 'They should be read aloud in good company – Norfolk company.'

That Friday session behind the microphone merely confirmed his qualities as a natural communicator and led to many return invitations to the studios. He embraced this new platform with the same relish characterising his classroom terms, pulpit calls as a popular lay reader and constant successes as dialect writer, performer and local historian.

His poems often took centre stage during entertainment rounds with my Press Gang over 25 years. They still call for enthusiastic airings during the annual celebration of our native tongue at Cromer when entrants take to the stage for praise and certificates.

In his 1973 foreword to *Tha's a Rum'un, Bor*, Dick Bagnall-Oakeley mused, 'This collection of Norfolk poems must surely be one of the very few, if not the only one, to be published this century.' He praised the verses for catching the true feel of country life with descriptions of events such as weddings, christenings, funerals and fetes.

Paving the way for *A Year Go By*, Eric Fowler said the Broad Norfolk of John Kett was the genuine article, 'not the interpretation of a literary gent or affection of a 'foreigner'. His hobbies of natural history, beekeeping, gardening and local history all embraced the rural theme ... and he sings his own songs at local concerts.'

Like comedian Sidney Grapes, who contributed the Boy John Letters to the *Eastern Daily Press*, John Kett happily combined written and spoken (or sung) entertainments in an appealing manner. And just like those evergreen epistles drawn from the very heart of Norfolk country life, JK's verses will enlighten and amuse for generations to come because they are unpretentious and enhanced by a gloriously durable dialect, never swamped by it.

His writing and performing stressed how a Norfolk man could have several sides, all of them equally challenging and uplifting. Employing his native tongue with its irrepressible humour and colourful vocabulary simply gave this village headmaster an extra qualification to impress.

This small selection from a prolific output starts with one of his specialties – festive verses wrapped up in dialect for *Eastern Daily Press* readers. This offering appeared on Christmas Eve, 1973:

GLAD TIDIN'S

This arternune I drawed along ter ar ole village scule;
Tha's savrel year ago since I went there.
An bor, tha's wholly chaanged, that hev – that med me feel a fule;
I felt right lorst at fust, I dew declare.

We hed an inviteertion t'hear the children sing,
An see thar little play – thar 'Chris'mus dew'.
My Missus, course she come along, she like that sort o' thing;
So we set down a little arter tew.

An I jus' said, that plaace ha' chaanged; all them long desks ha' gone.
An so's them ole oil lamps what give us light.
They'a got a lot more books an things I couln't maake naathin' on,
They fare as though they're fitted out oright.

Well, sune the boys an gals come in, an then my Missus say,
'John, there's a rea' lot on'em new ter me!'
There's such a crowd o' furriners now live aroun' this way,
Tha's suffin' haard t'know'em all, y'see.

But ar ole neerbour, she set nigh, an bor, she put us right.
She knew thar naames, an where they come from tew.
She's a read' maaster one, she is – ah, she don't miss a sight;
She know what all the village dew, she dew!

She showed us that there pair o' twins what come from York laast year
An that there little gal from Wisbech way.
There was three or four from Lunnon, an one from Devonshire,
An even one from Africa, she say.

Some others come from Scotland; they're up the faarm, y'see;
Their faather got a tidy bit o'ground.
They don't dew much fer Chris'mas, so he say t'me,
But New Year's Day he'a asked us t'go round.

Well, I set there, a-thinkin' back. So much come t'my mind
About the paast, an chaanges in ar ways.
An all ar worries, gret an small; I s'pose tha's haard t'find
A lot ter smile about in these here days.

I felt right low... then dew yew know, they all began ter sing;
An I looked up, an there them children stood.
An how they sung, newcomers tew! Why, bor, they fared t'bring
Rea' Chris'mas peace an love. That done me good...

'Glad tidin's o' gret joy'... tha's suffin' we don't orfen hear
When news come in from evrawhere each day,
An yit I b'leeve, at Chris'mas, as another year draw near,
A Little Child can bring that joy ar way...

THE OWLD LIFEBUTMAN

Dunt tork ter me o' the winter, boy
When the cold winds howl thru the trees
An' the raaindrops fallin' on my hid
Mearke my werry innards freeze
Fer I am gittin' old, my boy
Wi' a yearnin' fer the sun
Jest tew set an' sooak my tired ol' bunns
When the daaily wark is dun.

Dunt tork ter me o' the winter, boy
O' the skeartin' an' the snow
Carn't yew see I'm choucked rite up ter here
Cors I carn't git up an' go
Fer I am gittin' old, my boy
An' there's nut much left fer me
But a'dozin' orff in an eezy chair
Until death set me free.
Dunt tork ter me o' the ...wass that noise?
Thass a rockit, see the flare
Git outer my way, I'm orff ter the shore

There's a ship in trubble out there.

Dunt fuss now, git my oilskins down

Yew'd better put yors on tew

Now, never yew mind about my health

Cum on, there's wark ter dew.

'LIJAH'S HOSSES

'Cup, cup...cup-whoa!'... I haard the hosses tarn

An' stop, not far away from ar back door.

Then 'Lijah come up close agen the hedge;

I'd hear him holler, 'Wha's o'clock then, bor?'

An' I'd run in an' look at that ole clock;

There in the corner on a shelf that stood.

Then back I'd go, an' shout, 'Tha's jus' gone twelve',

An' 'Lijah, he'uld holler back, 'Tha's good!'

Then he'd git out the hosses' nosebags fust,

Afore he set right down agen them trees.

Took out 'is knife, a hunk o'crusty bread,

An' cut hisself a tidy lump o' cheese.

Not long he'd set there, 'fore he up agen,

Han's t'the plough, his back a little bent;

'Cup, cup there – wheesh!' I watched the furrer shine

Behind the team, as crorst the field they went,

Wi' flutt'rin' flocks o'seagulls allus nigh,

An' cryin' peewits tumblin' in the sky.

THE LITTLE GAL'S RABBIT

That died today,
That little white rabbit,
An she set there an cried.
That were her own,
Her pet, that rabbit;
She loved it. Then that died.

Poor little mawther,
She's on'y saven;
In't naathin' yew can say.
Tha's allus haard
T'larn, y'know...
God give: God taake away.

Maurice Woods

HARBERT'S HARVEST

One of the longest-running dialect adventures in newspaper history started with a challenge to find a likely companion for a much-admired champion of the hour.

The editor of the *Norwich Mercury* series of weekly publications wanted someone to write him a regular dialect feature to match the popularity of the Boy John Letters in the *Eastern Daily Press*. Maurice Woods, destined to become a leading figure in both local and national journalism, offered to give it a go.

'When he asked if I knew of anyone who might fit the bill, I told him I'd write it myself. He was extremely dubious but let me have a trial run,' said Maurice. The result was 'Harbert's News from Dumpton'. It ran for almost 40 years, clocking up about 1900 episodes.

Bred and born at Corton, near Lowestoft, Maurice started his long and distinguished newspaper career at the age of 18. He joined the *Lowestoft Journal* and, after army service during the second world war, edited the *Dereham and Fakenham Times*. He left his local patch to become a sub-editor on the *Manchester Guardian*.

In 1955, the editor-in-chief of the *Eastern Daily Press* lured him back to work in the London office. In due course Maurice became the paper's London editor, a post he held until retirement in 1980. During that period he served as chairman of the Parliamentary Press Gallery, chairman of the Newspaper Conference and chairman of the British section of the European Association of European Journalists.

Crowning moment of an outstanding career came with an invitation to Brussels to receive the European Prize for Journalism – an honour that must have been toasted with relish in the homely pubs of Dumpton and district.

A love of dialect blossomed naturally in childhood at Corton, where 'half the old men were fishermen and the other half farm labourers. As a schoolboy I used to earn a little pocket money by telling East Anglian stories at bowls club dinners and the like,' recalled Maurice.

Then he began writing in dialect more by accident than design as that weekly editor launched a new rural attraction in 1951, a sideline developing into a passionate marathon.

Maurice proved much more prolific than Sidney Grapes, composer of the Boy John epistles on an occasional basis, as he met a weekly deadline and spread his net wider to embrace a larger country cast from Dumpton and neighbouring communities.

He drew heavily on the kind of village characters and events dominating his childhood and early years on newspapers such as darts, football and cricket fixtures spiced with keen local rivalry, heated debates among colourful members of parish and rural district councils, eccentric clerics and pillars of the aristocracy and celebrated cases at the local magistrates' court.

Ironically, Maurice became an outspoken critic of those behind the campaign to keep broad Norfolk to the fore during the closing years of the 20th century, a movement culminating in the formation of Friends Of Norfolk Dialect in 1999.

Writing in the *Eastern Daily Press* six years earlier, Maurice said he had little patience 'with those who have lately been urging us to speak broad Norfolk. They are not conservationists, because there is little left to conserve. They are revivalists, unaware that language is what people speak, not what interfering romantics would like them to speak.'

The generations who spoke broad Norfolk belong to the past. Only a hint of their unfathomable pronunciation persists, together with a few local idioms and grammatical peculiarities, such as 'that do' for 'it does.'

Let us not delude ourselves. Broad Norfolk is well on the way to the limbo inhabited by the languages of Nineveh and Tyre. It cannot be summoned back.

I know Maurice saw – and heard – me as one of those 'interfering romantics' as I gave a constant platform to the dialect cause on BBC

Radio Norfolk's Dinnertime Show, lauded it on my entertainment rounds and led the attack on 'Mummerzet' tones infecting dramas alleged to be set in this part of the world.

Of course, he was following several other illustrious scribes who felt they had been in the vanguard of the 'last hurrah' train hurtling towards the tunnel to extinction. His 40-year journey in the company of ebullient Harbert, a rural correspondent with a roving ticket to amuse and impress readers all over the world, ought to have left scope for a hen's noseful or two of pride and optimism.

A couple of favourites from Harbert's massive file of weekly reports from Dumpton;

DAARTS IN RARE GOOD SPIRRITS
(First published October 30, 1964)

We're got tha ow Daarts Club a-goin agin at tha Fox, an this week we run over to tha Ticklin Green Man an gin em a troshin. I hent never sin a bunch o'daarts players as sorry for theirselves as what they wor when we'd done with em.

Mind yew, thet all help bein warm an dry when yew git thare. At one time we allers used to run over on our bikes, an thet never done us no good, not on a wet an rarfty ow night.

Howsomever, things a looked up a bit since then. Fred Johnson a got his ow car what he tearke some on us in, and Humpty Potter tearke tha rest on us in a 1929 Rolls Rice what he're bin imiteartin to sell but carnt git tha price he want.

'Thare's one thing,' I say to Humpty, as we give Fred Johnson a tow to git him staarted, 'thare's a rare good spirit in daarts. I hent never known tha time when them Ticklin players dint give us as much whisky as what we could drink to warm us up afore tha match begun.'

'Ah,' say Humpty.

* * *

Thass tha searme all round,' I say. 'Only thass rum they dish up as a rule at the King an Keys. I must a drunk a pint o'rum larst time I wor there. Thet must a corst em a forchune.'

'Thet corst us tha match,' say Humpty.

'Git out on it,' say tha boy Chaarlie.

'Thass right what I say, an yew know it,' say Humpty. 'Thare wornt a man among yer sober enough to hull a daart an hit a baarn door.'

'I wor a bit springy, I'm bound to admit,' I say. 'But thass as broad as thass long. If we coun't hull a daart streart, nor yit coun't they.'

'Dornt yew believe it,' say Humpty. 'They wor on beer time they wor pourin whisky down yar troot. They dornt dew it out o' tha kindness o' their harts, they dew it to win.'

'We won at Fumbleham, dint we?' say tha boy Chaarlie. 'Or Diddlin, I carnt remember which.'

'I ent surprised yew carnt remember,' say Humpty. 'Yew coun't remember yar nearme when I carried yew hoom, an thass a good job for yew I did carry yer hoom, cos yew coun't remember whare yew lived.'

'We'll win tonight, dew yew see,' I say.

'Not if yew lot dornt keep orf o' tha bottle we on't,' say Humpty.

'Consarn it all, Humpty,' say tha boy Chaarlie, 'whass tha good o' goin if yew carnt accept a bit o' hospitalita? If they want to hull their money away standin us whisky I ent a-goin to say no. Thet ent as if pearple orfered me whisky evera day o' my life.'

'Tha only time we won a match away,' say Humpty, 'wor when Fred Johnson sized up thet thare pickcher o' Queen Wictoria's Jewbilee what hung on tha wall alongside tha board, an aimed for tha Archbishop o' Canterberry evera time he wanted a double top.'

* * *

We dint none on us say a lot more till we pulled in at the Ticklin Green Man. Thare wor a good ow fire a goin in tha salune whare we play tha daarts matches, an all tha glarsses stood thare on the bar all ready for us, an them Ticklin fellers come round all friendly an staarted a-pourin out tha whisky.

'Hare we go agin,' say Humpty.

I reckon thet must a bin tha best paart of an hour afor we begun tha match. We wor all well warmed up by then, an thet struck me at tha time as bein a shearme we should hatter stop singin 'Nellie Dean' an staart hullin daarts about.

I wor feelin right on top o' my form myself, an I know tha whisky hent affected me, cos when I hulled a daart at tha' landlord's cat to git my eye in I only jest missed it.

Mind yew, thet thare landlord must a bin stood a few by his customers, cos tha way he took on about that thare cat, thet wornt normal.

* * *

I'll say this hare for Fred Johnson, he got all his daarts on tha board bar one, an then tha Ticklin captin hed a go. Now I allers dew say thare's some fellers what can tearke their beer an some what carnt. I know for a fack tha Ticklin captin hent hed above tew harves o'mild, an yit fust go orf he coun't hull his daarts for larfin.

'What tha hike are yew a-larfin at?' say young Bartie Tarner.

'Them cats!' say that Ticklin captin, 'Yew should a sin tha look on their kites when the boy Harbert hare hulled a handful o' daarts at em.'

'Whass tha matter with him?' arst tha boy Chaarlie.

'Them cats!' say tha Ticklin captin. 'Ho-ho-ho!'

'Thash shuffin what never shoun't – shoun't never – never shoun't be allowed on lishenshed premishesh,' say another o' them Ticklin fellers.

Then they all bust out larfin an we coun't stop em. In the finish that captin sung out 'Whisht!' an let fly with his daart, what went clean trew tha pickcher-cord holdin up a pickcher of a ship in full sail, an down thet come with a wallop.

'My hart alive,' I say to Humpty, 'they're warse than what we are.'

'They are, ent they,' say Humpty.

* * *

I never see a team play like it. What with larfin an singin an muckin about, thass a wonder they scored at all. We wornt any tew clever ourselves, but in tha finish we went hoom winners by a mile.

We dint hev a lot o' time to think about it on tha way hoom, cos Fred Johnson coun't drive streart, an we hed to keep on stopping to tow him out o' tha holls. But I did see Humpty countin some little ow green pills in a box, an thet struck me arterwards he must a put suffin in them Ticklin fellers' beer.

IN THET BOX IN THA BEWTS CAIRSE

(First published January 28, 1977)

We all hed a good squint at thet thare Roger Mainbrace Dimwood, what wor chaarged with nickin nine odd bewts, as he maarched inter tha Flitmarsh Court.

He wor thet nippy on his legs, he fared to look as if he could a won one o' them walkin rearces in that Olympicks.

Ow Mr. Lucas Miffler, tha chairman o' tha Bench, he set thare stammed.

'Thass a rummun,' he say, 'So far as what I can see, he dornt fare to himp. Did yew see him himp, Buncombe?'

'Himp?' say Buncombe. 'No, thet I dint.'

'Nor yit dint I,' say Fresher.

* * *

'Are yew sartain yew hent got narthin wrong with yar legs, Dimbrace?' arst Mr. Miffler.

'Wrong with my legs?' say Dimwood. 'Corse thare ent narthin wrong with my legs. I did hev a ingrowin toenearl once, but tha doctor cured it.'

'Well, I ent satisfied,' say Mr. Miffler. 'Dew yew roll yar trouser legs up a minnit – if Miss Crimp dornt mind. Yew can tarn yar glimmers tha other way, Miss Crimp, if yew want.'

Mr Jellicoe Hickey, o' Stott an Hickey, what wor there for tha defense, he shot out o' his chair like a rocket.

'Yar warships,' he sung out, 'this hare is all highly irregler. Thare ent narthin in tha rewles o' court prosedure what allow tha Bench to mearke my client roll his trouser legs up.'

'Oh, ent thare,' say Mr. Miffler. 'Well, bor, so far as what I'm consarned, thare ent narthin in tha rewles o' court prosedure to stop us. If tha Bench think thass in tha innerests o' justice to tearke a peark at tha offendant's legs, then justice a gotta be sarved.'

'May thet please yar warships,' shaarmed out Mr. Hickey, 'discreet inquiries consarnin tha steart o' my client's nether limbs are one thing. Mearkin him stand thare like a duzzy mawkin an roll his trouser legs up is another.'

'Trust yew lawyers to split hares,' say Mr Miffler. 'Yar pore father, rest his sole, he wor as bad as what yew are. He could argew black is white an git away with it.'

'As yar warship please,' say Mr. Hickey. 'But I submit thet I ent splittin hares when I remind tha Bench thet tha chaarge hent bin read out yit. If tha Bench regaard my client's legs as evidence, thass only right an proper they should give him a charnce to plead afore tha evidence is examined.'

'All in good time, Mr Stickey,' say Mr. Miffler.

'Even then, yar warships,' run on Mr. Hickey, 'I'll want to be conwinced as how evidence about my client's ankles, or carves, or knee-caps, or whatever thet is what a got tha Bench all steamed up, a got a bearin on tha cairse.'

'Alright, alright, keep yew yar wool on, Mr. Stickey,' say Mr. Miffler. 'I only wanted to know if he're got a wooden leg, thass all.'

* * *

Mr. Hickey opened his gob as if he wor a-goin to suggest thet Mr. Miffler hed a wooden hid, but he thowt better on it.

'I mean to say, if Bracewood hed a wooden leg, yew coun't say thet dint hev no bearin on tha cairse, could yer?' say Mr. Miffler. 'A feller with a wooden leg, he'd be jest tha sort o' feller what wanted to pinch odd bewts.'

'Like ow Jack Pinchin,' say Fresher Frogg.

'Who?' arst Mr. Miffler.

'Why, bor, ow Jack Pinchin, yew remember him,' say Fresher. 'He lorst a leg in tha Fust World War. Him an ow Ezra Beadle used to lean up agin tha front o' that Poost Orfice all day long.'

'I dornt see whare they come intew it,' say Mr. Miffler.

'Proper close friends they wor an all,' say Fresher. 'Ow Jack Pinchin hed lorst his left leg, an ow Ezra Beadle hed lorst his right, so they used to club together an buy one pair o' bewts betwixt em.'

139

'May thet please yar warships,' cut in Mr. Hickey, 'tha mutual arrearngement entered intew by Mr. Pinchin an Mr. Beadle dornt affeck my client. To searve farther argyment, may I arst yar warships to tearke thet from me thet my client's legs are as sound as what yars are.'

'What, booth on em?' arst Mr. Miffler.

'Booth on em,' say Mr. Hickey.

Mr. Miffler pulled his mustash an looked all of a nonplush like.

'Then what are them other exhibits in thet thare box, Inspeckter?' he arst.

'Skulls, yar warship,' say tha Inspeckter.

*　*　*

Yew should a hud tha 'oooohs' an 'aaaaashs' what went up in tha court when Inspeckter Churkey reckoned he'd got some skulls in tha box on tha tearble. Ow Mr. Miffler's gob dropped open, so did Fresher Frogg's, little Miss Crimp took orf har glarsses an stuck em back on agin, an Buncombe tha corn marchant, what hed dropped orf to sleep, he wook up with a staart.

'Skulls!' sung out Mr. Miffler. 'What, hev tha offendant bin a diggin up a charchyaard as well as nickin odd bewts?'

'No, yar warships,' say that Inspeckter. 'They're plarstick skulls.'

'My hart alive,' say Mr. Miffler, 'what with wooden legs an plarstick skulls, this hare cairse is a rummun, an no mistearke!'

THE WINDOW CLEANER

If yew gotta lotta windas in yar house,
Yar bound t'hev a call,
From a bloake what live jist down the rud,
Who's the cheekiest onnem all.

Now ev'ry day, he'll be down yar way,
With his trusty ole washleather,
Whistlin' away, come rearn or shoine,
'Cos he en't troubled by no weather.

Up his ladder he dew climb,
To the last rung, ever so high,
If yew've got new cartins, he's the fust t'know,
For nuffin' dun't miss his eye!

Then he'll be a-knockin' on yar door,
Demandin' his three-an'-six,
With cash in his pocket, he's orf loike a flash,
There's no-one move quite s'quick!

Jist look at yar windas, ever so clean,
A sparkle on ev'ry pearne,
What a blummin' wearst o' money that is,
'Cos – blust me, tha's started to rearn!

(Ashley Gray, Wymondham, 2007)

141

Colin Riches

BIBLE RICHES

Methodist minister Colin Riches gave familiar Bible stories a Norfolk coat of paint in the 1970s and attracted fresh flocks of admirers to the 'divine dialect' department.

He was invited by Anglia Television to broadcast a series of stories in broad Norfolk in their 'Bible for Today' epilogue programme. This led to publication of *Dew Yew Lissen Hare*, a collection of New Testament favourites, and *Orl Bewtiful an New*, a similar salute to the Old Testament.

'People have said the Bible sounds more homely when it comes over in broad Norfolk and their favourable comments have encouraged me to regard this exercise as a worthwhile extension to my ministry' Colin told me as he reflected on early influences for using the dialect in this way.

'Hearing Bernard Miles telling Bible stories on the radio in his delightful Hertfordshire accent set me wondering whether it would be possible to do the same thing in our not dissimilar Norfolk accent. Then there was Sidney Grapes. Having been minister for eight years in the Martham Circuit, which includes his native village of Potter Heigham, I found the idea of doing such a thing more and more attractive.'

Colin also broadcast dialect stories in Anglia's 'Highway' programme and in BBC Television's 'Songs of Praise' from the legendary Christmas show at Thursford, in the heart of the Norfolk countryside. He was a regular contributor to BBC Radio's 'Pause for Thought' from 1976, first with Roundabout East Anglia and then with Radio Norfolk from its first week of broadcasting in September, 1980.

Born in Norwich, Colin considered himself 'city' rather than 'country' until a friend at Bracondale School asked him to spend a summer holiday helping with the harvest on his father's farm.

'That's where my country education began,' he reflected. 'I got blisters on my hands, learned what a coomb of wheat felt like on my back as I staggered up the barn steps with it and actually drove an old Fordson tractor a few yards.

'But more importantly on this farm at Shotesham All Saints I gained a love of the country, was introduced to the Methodist Church and learned some Norfolk words and phrases. Now, looking back, the blisters, coombs of wheat and Fordson tractor have gone – but country life, its accents, and Methodism have stayed.'

In his preface to *Dew Yew Lissen Hare*, he admitted the task of writing 20,000 words in dialect was not an easy one. 'We Norfolk people, naturally, know how to say in our own way the word "road", but how exactly do you spell it? No doubt my spelling of it and other words differs from the way other writers would have chosen. If this is the case, I take refuge in the fact that there is as yet no definitive glossary of correctly spelt Norfolk words!'

He leans delightfully on memories of old Methodist lay preachers illuminating sermons with homely parables of their own, some of them packed with unintentional humour. For example: 'One brother was talking about John the Baptist who, though Herod beheaded him, had a triumphant end, for in the words of the preacher, "orf John went to heaven; no hid on".'

Another well-worn story tells of the preacher who in a sermon about heaven warned his congregation thus: 'Some o' yew'll hatta watch it dew yew oon't never git te heaven te blow on them thare harps, and somne o'yew what dew git thare'll see harps standin thare what hint never been blew.'

Colin Riches enjoyed what the Rev Edward Gillett had done just over a century earlier, turning the Song of Solomon into the Norfolk tongue, but realised there was a far bigger picture to colour:

Many Bible stories slip almost naturally into the Norfolk style, happily without running the risk of sounding irreverent, and I can vouch for their regular effectiveness and fresh entertainment value after featuring them for several years in travelling productions like All Preachers Great and Small for local churches.

Congregations seem genuinely reassured that God can speak with a clear Norfolk voice. Well, he did holler at the Creation: 'Le's hev some loight on the job.'

ORL BEWTIFUL AN NEW

*(Title chapter from the collection of Old Testament stories,
first published in 1978)*

Yew moight a' knew that if thare wus gorn te be annerone thare in the beginning that'd be God. He int the sort te let things go b'chance.

'Thare's gorn to be some sense o'parpose in this hare warld, d'yew see if thare int'. Thass what he say, an thass how't wus.

But fer a start there woont narthen livin. The arth that dint hev ne shearpe, an thare woont narthen livin nowhare. An te top the lot that wus dark, whooly dark, pitch dark, so's yew coont see a mortal thing.

But then, the wind fare te git up, 'til a gearle wus blowin. An if yew'd 'a said, 'Hallo, God, he's a starrin hisself,' yew'd 'a bin roight, 'cause out o' that wind what swep through iverything, thare come a gret voice what hollered out: 'Orroight, come on. Le's hev some loight on the job'. An, d'yew know what? Soon as he give the order thare wus loight iverawhare, just as though someone'd tarned on some gret switch.

'Thass batter,' God say, rubbin his eyes, 'We kin see what we're a'dewin on now'.

But he wornt no fule. He knew yew'd hatta git some kip. So he kep some darkness by'm. The loight he called 'day', and the darkness he called 'noight'. 'D'yew foller each other loike that thare,' God say tew'm. An thass how thass bin ever since; day an noight; toime and toime agin.

The next bit o' sortin out God done wus with the water. He dint want'd wet iverawhare, so he gathered the water tergather in the lows, an thass how yer gret seas an learkes come about. Then, when orl that water dreamed inter the lows, yew got yer dry land, dornt yer see? God called that 'arth', an the waters what he brought tergether he called 'seas'.

Then, ow God, he stood back, an he looked at what he'd done, an he say, 'Yiss,' he say, 'Yer a comin on, but I shell hatta tricolearte yew up a bit ... Le's hev a few trees an plants about; an a bit o' colour. Yiss, wha' bout some flowers?'

Then he thought te hisself, 'I'd loike some grass about too; that'd look noice an thass good fer feed'. So, arter a bit orl this bewtiful stuff started a comin up, an ow God, he wus thare o'course encouraging on it. 'Come on, dew yer stuff,' he'd say, 'Grow yer seeds, an the wind'll scatter'm orl about.'

Cor, yew ought 'a sin the chearnge! Ow God, he looked at'd, an he say, 'Phewa, that wus a job an a harf, but that look a soight batter than afore. Yiss,' he went on, pleased at what he see, 'Yer a comin on roight noice.'

An', o'course, yew know as well as I dew, that the warld, whass se marvellous an bewtiful, an full o'loife, dint happen in foive minutes. That wus years a gittin loike that. But the thing wus, ow God wus thare the whoole o' the toime. He hed the jurisdiction on it. Narthen dint come about b'chance; God see t'that.

He see the sun thare, a shinin away, giving loight an loife durin the day. 'Thass the style,' he smoiled an say. Then, out come the moon, an the stars they come out a twinkling. 'Thare's a whoole lot thare for'm te look at an think about,' he say noddin his hid. 'Thass just how I wanted it.'

Then God, he looked over the seas, an he say, 'We could dew with a bit o' loife down thare'. So he mearde orl them creatures what live in the water. From gret ow whearles te li'ow winkles. From sharks te shrimps. Fish b' the thousand. 'Thare y'are,' he say, 'orf yew go an dew yer stuff.'

An then he filled up the seas an the rivers, he looked up te the sky, an he thought, 'We could do w' some bardds up thare'. So his next job wus mearkin orl different koinds o' bardds; swans an starlins, hawks and harnsers, sparrers an eagles, an a whoole lot more. They grew an spread their wings an flew orf orl over the plearce.

Seeing that mearde him se happy; he rearzed his hands up an arms up, an shouted tew'm orl: 'Thass roight, moy bewties; orf yew go... yer got the whoole new warld te fly in.'

Then God gearzed over orl the lands: some high, some low, some hot some cold: desert, jungle, marsh, forest, snowy wearstes an rocky mountains; an slow-loike, with a whoole lot o' care an thought an love, he mearde the animals what wus suited te orl them different plearces. Polar bears an hosses, he mearde, bishy barnybees an bullocks, lions an tigers, elephants an kangaroos; my hart, if ow God dint enjoy hisself. He dint hev narthen te go by, so he could please hisself what he done. An he did. Orl shearpes an soizes. Yew kin imagine how busy he wus when yew think o' giraffes an snearkes, frogs an rabbit, pigs an monkeys. No ind o'ideas he hed. An when he see'm orl a jumpin an crawlin, hoppin an swimming, climbin trees an burrowing inter the arth, even ow God drew his breath back.

'Blow me,' he say, 'I recken thass blummun marvellous. I sharnt ever be loonely with this little lot.'

But, come the next morning, God, he set down an thought about what he'd mearde, an he say te hisself, 'Thare's suffun missin ... I know. Thare int ne people about! We carnt hev a warld w' no people in it'. So, with his hid in his hands, he thought hard fer a long, long toime. Then he mearde a man.

An he dint harf put some thought inter him, I'll tell yer. Mearde man loike hisself he done. Give him a soul so's he could dream an think an plan, an wark out ideas. Mearde him so's he'd apprecieate bewty and truth, an know what love wus orl about. An he mearde a woman too, ter be man's loife partner.

An when that farsst couple stood on their feet, ow God blessed them more'n what he'd done annerthing else.

'Out yew go,' he say tew'm, 'This hare warld, the whoole on it, thass yers. Yer gotta a bewtiful new warld to live in with iverathing that yew want. So moind yew look arter it an treat'd roight.'

Then, them two looked up at God, an they promised him they'd dew what he wanted.

Out they went. An when God see'm go, thare wus a tear come in his eye, 'cause they were his special creartion, dornt yer see? His children, yew moight say.

An loike any proper father, he wondered how they wus a gorn te git on, how they'd behearve.

'Fore he went te sleep that noight, he thought over an over agin about what he'd done in mearkin man. An suffun fare te tell him that wus the best day's wark he ever did dew.

'Thass good,' God say, contented loike, 'Yiss, thass verra good, I reckon'.

THAT FOREIGNER WHAT DONE SUFFUN

*(From Dew Yew Lissun Here, a collection of New Testament
stories first published in 1978)*

One day, an ow lawyer, what thought he knew better than Jesus, say te
him, 'Whass orl this hare about eternal loife? How ken I git'd?'
'Wodda that say in the law?' Jesus answered, 'What've yew larnt from
your readin on it?' 'That say,' reployed the lawyer, 'yer gotta love the
Lord your God with orl yer hart, an soul, an with orl the strength yer got
in yer. An yer gotta love yer nearber loike yerself.'

'Thass roight, moy man,' smoiled Jesus, 'Yer got'd. Dew yew dew
that, then you'll live.'

But the ow lawyer, he dint fare te be satisfoid, so he questioned Jesus
agin.

'Yiss', he say, 'Thass orl very well, but who is moy nearber?'

'Set yew down a minute,' Jesus say, 'an I'll tell yew a tearle.'

This hare is what he say.

A chap wuz a walkin along the rood from Jerusalem te Jericho. Rough
ow rood that wuz: full o' twists an tarns, an gret ow rocks along soide on
et where robbers could hoide. Not the sort o plearce te go on yer own.
Roight enough, this hare chap wuz beat up by some roughs. Took his
money they done, nicked his overcoot, then left him a layin thare, more
dead'n aloive.

Now, that so happened that a li'll learter a priest come along that way.
Thinkin noice thoughts he wuz, an a wondrin what he talk about in his
sarmon next Sundee. This hare priest, he see that poor chap what'd bin
beat up, and dew yew know what? The farsst thing he say te hisself wuz,
'Now, howd yew hard,' he say. 'That wornt dew fer me te touch him, dew
if I dew I shornt be clean, accordinlie te the law, for a week or more. Then
who dew the preachin come Sundee?' He knew his Bible, dornt yer see.
So, stret away, he crorssed over the rood, and went past on the other soide.
Thass what he done.

Then, blow me, a couple o' minutes learter, an ow Levite, he come
down the rood too. He see the chap a layin thare. Up he go an hev a look.
Cautious loike. Thare wornt no flies on him. An he say te hisself, he say,

'Now, that wornt dew fer me te go pookin around hare, dew if I dew I moight fall inter a trap. Howd I know thare ent some crook behoind them rocks, watchin me? Out he moight come an, cor he moight gimme sich a clout acrorss the skull what'd harf dew me in. No, I ent a getting involved.' So arter he looked, orf he went. That dint worry him, that poor bloke a layin thare.

Then, learter still, someone else come along that rood. He wuz a traveller what come that way orfen, an he hed a ow dicky w'him. Now he wornt a Jew. He wuz a Samaritan. An the thing wuz, them Jews dint hev narthen te dew with them Samaritans. Fact, they wuz allwuz a mobben about them. They reckoned they dint have no roight te be in their country. Fer years the Jews hed bin raw about this. 'They want te git back te whare they belong: blummun harf casts!' Thass how they talked about them.

So annerway, down this hare rood come this hare foreigner what dint never oughter bin thare. He see that chap a layin thare, a holdin his hid, an groanin away. Blood iverywhare thare wuz. An dew yew know what he done? Crorssed over loike them other two...? No, that he dint. He bent down, an he say, 'Wha they done te yew, ow partner?' Then he bandidged him up as best he could, lifted him on te his ow dicky. Then, ever se careful, he mearde his way te the nearest pub what done bed an breakfast. He orfen stayed thare hisself.

He got some help an carried the poor chap indoors and settled him down in bed. Than that foreigner he say te the landlord, he say, 'Dew yew look arter him, an give him orl what he need te git well. Hare's a fiver. If yew spend annermore, dew yew let me know when I come this way agin, an I'll mearke et roight.'

'Thass moy tearle,' say Jesus. 'Now, who dew yew think wuz the proper nearber te the chap what got done over?'

'The foreigner, o'course,' say the lawyer. 'The one what done suffun.'

'Thass roight,' say Jesus roight smart. 'So, orf yew go, an dew the searme.'

TASTY CAPTURE

'What a clever little man,' she said, her face all crumpled up with smiles. 'Catchin' a rabbit in the piece like that, why he must have gone a lamperin' over them quicks like nobody's business. I shan't stint for wittles while he's here, that I on't. I on't be needin' to eke out with swimmers like Mrs Liddamore, allus fillin' her men up wi' turnips or plump or dumplins, or old muck like that room o' good quality meat, mind you I got nawthin' against dumplins when tha's parky weather. Tha's a good fat little old buck rabbit – we'll have him Friday and you kin have a nice bit o'hinderpart Duffy boy.'

David Holbrook, *Getting it Wrong with Uncle Tom*, 1998).

THE SCHOOL PHOTOGRAPH

Thet hung on thuh wall in thuh classroom
In a place where awl could see
Marked on it wi' a red arrer
Wus Harry, an' Billy an' me.

Thuh red arrer wus a reminder
Or so thuh teacher sed
Of past misdeeds an' toime wastin'
We thowt had gone over his head.

Along wi' abowt thatty others
We left school at fourteen we three
Lessons now orl forgotten
Thass wark for Harry, an' Billy, an' me.

As oi now plough a lonely furrer
Oi think o' thet photo on thuh wall
An' wish I'd a lissened tew thuh teacher
Insted o' thinkin' oi knew it orl.

Norfolk Tales by Bruther Will, 1981

Old Barney

RUSTIC RACONTEUR

The old reminder that 'the best pictures are on the wireless' never rang more true than during the first seven years of my career with BBC Radio Norfolk.

I masqueraded as the new station's rural correspondent travelling into the city every Saturday morning on a trusty old bike to address thousands of listeners with a heady mix of dialect and humour. I still bump into people who thought Old Barney was a real person.

Yes, a vibrant example of what you can get away with over the airwaves – and anything had to be possible after ventriloquist Peter Brough and his well-dressed schoolboy dummy entertained the nation with Educating Archie during the 1950s. They could honestly claim you never saw their lips move.

Old Barney was created in the bar of a London hotel where members of the original Radio Norfolk team relaxed after training sessions. I was goaded into rustic party pieces, not least to offer colleagues from other parts of the country a little taste of delights to come when the station opened in September, 1980. They wanted a bit more than another chorus of 'Hev Yew Gotta Loight, Boy?'

Inspired mainly by the Boy John Letters and Harbert's News from Dumpton in local newspapers from childhood, Old Barney became my alter ego on home soil. He could express and enhance blatantly parochial views that might have drawn sharp rebuffs from the BBC hierarchy if presented in a more serious and orthodox style. A little bit o'squit can go a long way!

More an observer of others than a character anxious to talk about himself, the retired farm worker started every broadcast with the same greeting, 'Mornin' ter orl on yer' and wrapped up each one with his still-popular catchphrase 'Dew yew keep a'troshin'!' His village pub, the Datty Duck, inspired the bulk of his material. He carried no-nonsense views on the way country life was changing – a constant theme in dialect deliveries – and so served as a useful social commentator for most of the 1980s.

I wrote and recorded those Saturday morning reflections on the afternoon or evening before to ensure a topical flavour. On a couple of occasions Old Barney mastered sufficient technology to phone in when his bike was stolen or he got a puncture. (I think he once reported the theft of his bike to Interplod).

Scripts from the first two years behind the microphone were transformed into three highly successful volumes, *Dew Yew Keep a'Troshin'*, *Down at the Datty Duck* and *Dunt Fergit Ter Hevver Larf*. A cassette was also produced with a selection of his rustic tales.

Running two or three words into each other became a regular Old Barney habit. A few examples; 'I suppose' becomes 'spooz' – 'going to' is 'gorter' or 'gorta' – 'a bit of' is shortened to 'bitter' – 'must have retired' turns into 'muster retyred' and 'in front of' is abbreviated into 'frutter'. There are obvious discrepancies in style and spelling – but they merely add spice to the rural mixture.

Many words beginning with the letter 'v' are given a 'w' start instead, like 'willuj' for 'village' and 'wicker' for 'vicar'. A highly individual style is emphasised in lines like: 'Dunt yew paggarter orl his skwit'. A clinical translation provides; 'Don't pay any regard to all his nonsense.' He also invents a lot of his own words and phrases, but most are easy to follow in the context of what he's talking about.

'Coronearshun milk' comes out of a tin; 'HelterSkeltzer tablets' go frothy in the glass. 'The defective van' checks if you have a television licence. 'Triculearted lorries' make a lot of noise. 'A partishun' goes round the pub for regulars to sign. They form a 'willujanty' movement to take on the brewery. Straightforward derivation – 'We live in this heer willuj... an weer anty cloosin the Datty Duck.'

In his unassuming way, Old Barney proved a dual-purpose champion of the dialect cause with rallying calls on air and in print. He introduced a host of listeners to broad Norfolk while putting over sentiments about the changing face of the county with which they could readily identify.

Perhaps that is his lasting legacy, an outspoken ambassador for those trying to protect precious qualities of local life during a period of irrevocable change. And he laced it all with sly humour and an open invitation to see the best pictures on the wireless.

OLD BARNEY ARRIVES

(Broadcast just before midday on Saturday, September 13th, 1980, two days after the official opening of BBC Radio Norfolk, this was Old Barney's debut as the station's rural correspondent, a role he filled for seven years. This also featured as the opening chapter in *Dew Yew Keep a 'Troshin!*, first volume of Old Barney's broadcasts published in 1984.)

Mornin' ter orl on yer. Spooz fast thing yew're gorta arsk is how a country bor lyke me kin git his own little spot on thole wireless. Well, I kin arnser that wun pretty sharpish. This heer lot on Reardyo Norfik watted sumwun wi' thar lug ter the grownd deep in th' harter the country, and yew hatta be up fearly arly in the mornin' ter catch me owt when that cum ter raral 'fairs.

Ire bin cloos ter the soyl orl my loife, an I reckon I know b'now wot mearke us tick owt heer. We dew hoss itter Norridge now an' gin ter dew a bitter shoppin an garp rown the market, but thass allus nyce ter git hoom, put yer ole feet up an git the kittle on.

Summer them yung'uns, speshlly them bitser mawthers orl dolled up wi' thar oiy shadder an' that, they ent satisfied wi' a nite down the pub or a bitter skwit at the willuj darnse. They cleer orf ter them diskothews ter git deffened an' gollop rown in thar fansy clobba. Oi artner nockin' onnem. They're gotta spend thar munny on suffin, I spooz, but yew dunt go a lot on that sorta thing if yew're bin up sinse afore six in the mornin', a'milkin' thole cows and then gittin the harvest in.

Now I'yre retired lyke, I dew hev a bitter tyme ter hop on m'byke an' corl on summer my ole meartes. We wuzzer clackin' thuther day bowt harvests o'yeers ago when we fast started wak. Orl them bewtiful hosses an' luvly little boinders ... that wuz wholly qwyet longside these heer combines an' driers they hev terday.

Thass rearl point, yer know, we got the job dun jest the searme, even if that did tearke a bit longer. Summer them fewls wot chearse bowt till they jest bowt meet tharselves a'cummin' back, orl they finish up with is a koronary. I'yre sin sum on'em beltin trew the willuj orf the mearn rood in thar smart new Cerpryse. Hent gotta minnet ter live, moost onnem – an' they dunt zakly tearke root in the pub if they dew fynd tyme ter drop in fer a harf.

Oonly tyme they say 'Are yew gorta hev wun?' is when they're blomin' lorst! An' yit, they're the wuns wot tearke the jews owter us an' say weer ahynd the tymes an' livin in the parst. Praps we dunt hoss 'long lyke that Steve Ovett – heel bust a gut afore heer dun – an' we sartanly dunt git ahynd rest o'orl them cars on Bank Hollerdays, or go ter Frarnse an' hoop we kin git back b' Chrismuss!

Yeh, we dew tearke't bit moor eezy, thass why yer see ser menny ole boys lookin' sharp an' fuller beenz down the Datty Duck. They tearke it eezy, speshlly when thass thar tann ter gitter rownd in. We did berry ole Jearcub Stearnes larst Thassday. But that wunt much orrer sprize rearly. He wuz ded...

So, dunt fergit... that ent them wot go the kwickest wot git things dun the best. Yewre gotta hev tyme fer a larf anner bitter yap, hent yer? Thass bin my motto sinse I fast wenter muckspreadin' longa ole Horry Mason. 'No need ter go barmy, bor' he say ter me. 'Yewre gotta hev a bitter enjy left ter lift that pynt Oim gorta buy yer.' He nivver did, but that larnt me a good lessun orl the searme.

Oill hev nuvver little yarn wiyyer next week. Thankyer muther fer the rabbit. Mynd how yew go, and dunt yew fergit yew lot. Dew yew keep A'troshin!

A RYTE GOOD DEW!

(Old Barney's last bulletin to go into print hit the airwaves on June 5th, 1982.He brought a full exclusive report on the village wedding of his best friend, Cloddy Gates, and retired district nurse, Flossie Crabtree, a comparative newcomer on the scene who 'torked proper'. This also featured as the final chapter in *Dunt Fergit Ter Hevver Larf!* third and last volume of Old Barney's broadcasts published in 1986.)

Mornin' ter orl on yer. Sorry moi voice is bit sorfter, but ter tell yer the honist trewth Iyre still got skullearke. An that unt cum as no spryze ter enny onnem wot wuz selebreartin at the weddin twin Cloddy and Flossie.

Cor, we dint harf hev trubbel longer Dinger Bell. Tyme I git back ter Datty Duck larst Satterday dinnertime, he wuz hallerin an darnsin. Beer orl down his weskut, an heed lorst his tiepin. Good job he hent got ner teef, cors hell know wot heeder dun tymes he went in an owter lavetry.

Gibby Painter wuz misrubel cors he hatter fork owt fer new jackit; he got marryed in thuther wun heer got wi' patches on them sleeves an cuffs orl freard.

His missus looker treet wi' har new hat owter club book. Pappel job an sprigger himlock or suffin stickin owt onnit. Pappel dress anorl wot nearly fitted har – look mor lyke jarrer damsun jam. We cleened Dinger up best we cood an took him rownd ter Flossie so she kin sort him owt. I corled fer Cloddy an we strowl down the rood.

'Dew yew know,' he say, 'Nivver thowt Iyd dew this. I ent narvus. Iym num. Got ner feelin nowhere. Funny, entit, thass larst tyme Iyll walk down heer single blook. Rum job arter orl them years.' He wuz still clackin ter hisself tyme we git down frutter the chatch an weartin forrit orl ter happin.

'Here cum the bryde!' Blarst, she look bitter orryte in har gown, wi' Dinger holdin on fer orl hees wath – an that enter lot. Bit lyker oshun lyner wi' tugboot longsyde. Me an Cloddy git owr bits ryte, an parsun giv little yarn bowt pullin tergether an bildin howse. Marruj, he say, thass bit lyke putting roof on arter yewre got the worls an winders up. I nudje itter Cloddy an say, 'Ah, yewre got yar roof on, boy. Jest yew mearke sartan them tyles dunt blow orff when the wind start howlin!' He larf.

That wuz orff ter willuj horl fer the grub an speechifying, but we hatter dew wi'owt Dinger cors yer coont git ner sense owter him arter heer downed twetty bottles. He kipped orff an we leeve him owt back wheer they mearke sandwidjes. Pitter bowt his speech, cors that took us long tyme ter wryte it owt in big letters so he kin reed it.

Cloddy med feer job onnit, thow Flossie did prompt him now an agin. She shew har booklarnin wi' sum propper toosts afore I git ter mer feet an hev few wads. I thank the parsun fer tannin up an Mrs Claypole on thorgun fer gittin tewns in ryte order – Fyte the Good Fyte an Rescew the Perrsishin. That med em orl larf.

I tan ter ole mearte Cloddy an say, 'They tell us theers bullit owt there wi' yar nearme onnit, but I dint spect yew ter git the canon anorl.' Flossie dint say noffin, but dunt rekun she tearke tew kindly ter that perscripshun.

Darnsin an drinkin till gone ten, but we dint hev raffle cors that dint seem ryte. Flossie went ter chearnj itter har gornway clobber, an smart she look anorl. Mr and Mrs Gates say feer yer well bowt twetty ter ten, an thass fast tyme Iyre sin Cloddy anxshus ter git way frum the beer.

Taxi weartin, an orff they go fer hunnycoom at Hunstun wheer he ewsed ter go when he wuz kid at Sundy Skool. She lyke thole plearse anorl.

An thassit. Hatter larf at gret ole bulloon tyed ter backer the taxi. That say: 'Newley weds, chearnjer beds ... And dew yew keep a'troshin!'

PEDLAR JOHN

Now, then, togather, this here then is the true tearl a' John Chapman, the Pedlar a' Swaffham, and how he did of old time find gret treasure.

Years and dickies a' years ago, long time afore yew and me was born, old John he lived in a little old bit of a shant jest orf the Market Square with Keartie his wife, two titty totty boys, a little bearby mawther and his dorg.

Accordin' to all accounts he wuz a werry well respected, Godfarin' and chachgoin' man, who arnt an honest livin' b'traipsin round all over the shute from door t' door a buyin' and a sellin' all mander a' things in the hamlets and willages round about.

Him and his good leardy was borth as happy as the day was long and all content, till one night he drempt this dream.

He drempt it the once and dint pay no regard, but the second time he began to axt hisself if there mightn't be suffin in it arter all, and when he drempt it for the thadd time, well bor he knew right well there must be.

He heerd this voyce in his dream, y'see, tellin' on him t'go and meark his way up to London and stand on London Bridge and there, that said, should be told unto him good tidin's to his adwantage.

You may depend he dint wait f'no second biddin. So, without n'more t'dew, the next d'y morn he wuz up with the lark and bad his wife a fond farewell, then orf he go with his dorg at his heels and his staff in his hand to London Town.

(Reg Drake, Pedlar of Swaffham, Norfolk Fair, 1976)

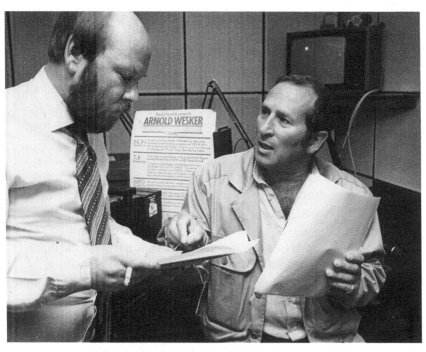

*Keith Skipper (left) and Arnold Wesker prepare for
the world premiere of 'Sugar Beet'.*

WESKER'S WAY

Arnold Wesker, one of the key figures of 20th century drama, not only put Norfolk on an international stage but also made genuine attempts to give his players proper Norfolk voices. So he is entitled to an enthusiastic curtain call for undertaking a bold mission in direct contrast with the bulk of productions allegedly set in the county.

'Roots' opened at the Belgrade Theatre in Coventry in May, 1959, with Joan Plowright cast as the drama's central character, Beattie Bryant. Wesker provided notes on pronunciation:

> This is a play about Norfolk people. It could be a play about any country people and the moral could certainly extend to the metropolis.
>
> But as it is about Norfolk people it is important that some attempt is made to find out how they talk. A very definite accent and intonation exist and personal experience suggests that this is not difficult to know.

He points out that when the word 'won't' is used, the 'w' is left out. It sounds the same but the 'w' is lost. Double 'ee' is pronounced as in 'it' – so that 'been' becomes 'bin' etc. 'Have' and 'had' become 'hev' and 'hed'. 'Ing' loses the 'g' so that it becomes 'in' and 'bor' is a common handle, a contraction of neighbour.

Instead of the word 'of', Norfolk people say 'on' – e.g. 'I've hed enough on it' and 'What do you think on it?' Their 'yes' is used all the time and sounds like 'year' with a 'p' – 'yearp.' 'Blast' is also in common usage and is pronounced 'blust', a short sharp sound as in 'gust'. The cockney 'ain't' becomes 'ent' – also short and sharp. The 't' in 'that' and 'what' is left out to give 'thaas' and 'whaas', e g. 'Whaas matter then?'

If Wesker could take such trouble to come up with a useful guide, why have so many writers, actors and dialect coaches failed lamentably to point anywhere towards an authentic Norfolk sound? Well, he did have some valuable background experience: he worked in Norfolk during the early 1950s, living with relatives at Wacton, near Long Stratton. As well as a spell as a kitchen porter at the Bell Hotel in Norwich, Wesker worked on the land, joined a firm laying huge pipes in the road and became a seed sorter in the maltings at Pulham St Mary. He tried to establish himself as a freelance journalist but only two articles appeared in print.

One of those that 'got away' allowed me to thank him personally for setting such a good example in his pursuit of the real Norfolk sound. He was back in the area in October, 1984, for a special week of events initiated by BBC Radio Norfolk. I organised the world premiere of something he wrote over 30 years earlier while working in the county.

'Sugar Beet' is a dialogue between two farm labourers as they put their backs into it up and down the rows. Wesker penned it in 1953 and claims it was turned down by the *Eastern Daily Press*. I deemed it worthy of a wider audience although the agricultural scene it portrays has long disappeared.

Wesker did the scene-setting while his nephew, Keith Keeble, and I had the starring roles on the Dinnertime Show. There had been scope for just a couple of rehearsals in the Radio Norfolk kitchen, appropriately enough. The evening before we had joined the author and his wife, Dusty from Starston, for a production of 'The Kitchen' at Norwich's Maddermarket Theatre. That play has its roots in Wesker's experiences at the city's Bell Hotel and at restaurants in London and Paris.

He was pleased with the treatment of 'Sugar Beet' and didn't mind when I took several liberties with his script. Indeed, he gave me permission to make any amendments I pleased and to publish in this celebration of all things Norfolk as a tribute to those who have relished the rigours of knockin' and toppin'.

Knighted in 2006 for services to the theatre, he was made an Honorary Doctor of Literature by the University of East Anglia 17 years earlier – a measure of the esteem in which he has long been held in an area which inspired some of his best work.

SUGAR BEET

Sheez knockin' well terday.

Yeh. Wunt werry wet overnyte, wuz it?

No, Look like thass gorter be fair owd day.

Yeh. Them beet'er droy ter mornin'

They are anorl. Knock easy, dunt there?

Yeh. Dunt dew ter hev it tew wet overnoyte, dew it? Tew hevvy.

Big anorl, arnt ther?

Yeh.

Mearke hevvy gowin when that owd mowld cling ter't.

Yeh...dunt dew ter hev'em tew hevvy orl day. Ruff on th'owd rists.

Yeh.

But thass good job terday. Mowld forl orff easy. Iyre known this fild
when that wuz shin deep in mud. Shin deep, I tell yer. An we hatter push
th'owd cart anorl cors the tractor got stuck.

Yeh.

Yeh. An they're hed frorst onnem tew.

But sheez knockin' orryte terday.

*The seven o'clock sun came up red over the huge, flat field of green
beet as the two men bent down again to the next row.*

Member that Lunnuner wot wakked here larst yeer?

That wuz afore my tyme, wunt it?

When'd yew come then?

March o'this yeer.

Jist afore yar tyme, then. He wuz here three munth afore Chrismuss.
Yeh, dint stay ner longer. Hed nuff arter fast cuppler days on sugar beet.

Yeh?

Yeh. He say ter owd Buckley,' he say, 'Blarst, this ent no test fer
manhood – this heer's test fer insannerty!' An owd Buckley he say ter this
heer chap, he say, 'Yew'd better pack up then.' An he say, 'Yeh, rekun Iyd
better.' He dint larst long! Kweer sorter chap he wuz. He say ter me, he
say, 'Dunt they hev mershines ter dew this heer job?' An I say they hev

mertshines orrite but that wunt dew fer Buckley ter hev enny cors he wunt want nun o'us then.

No, that he wunt, thass trew nuff. Hev a mershine fer the beet an Buckley wunt hev us go arter 'em in the winter. He'd send us arter the barley an thass the lot fer us fer the yeer.

I tell him that.

Wod he say then?

Huh! He dunt say noffin; he jist pull a fearse an carry on arter the beet, an I arsk him when he git hoom, is he gorter dew enny gardnin'?

An wod he say ter that?

He dunt rekun thass funny cors he say, 'We hent gotter garden!'

The long rows of beet leaves shook in the wind and the piles of knocked beet lay, neatly rowed, ready for topping; pale lines along the brown earth. Somewhere over the morning the eight-ten train hummed, and fifty minutes later the nine o'clock train hooted by and the two men stopped for tea and thick sandwiches.

Thass fair owd job this weather. Buckley rekun we're gorter hev Indyan summer.

No tellin' is theer?

No, there ent.

Wot wuz that Lunnuner dewin down heer, then?

Come ter wakk on the land, he say. He hev sum fun gorn arter the harvist, but sewn's ever he started on the beet, blarst he hed nuff!

Yeh?

Yeh. He finished up so he wuz on orl fours. 'Back-brearkin', barstud job!' he say. 'Back-brearkin', hart-brearkin' an sowl-destroyin'!' he say. They wuz his wads. He'd start fresh in the mornin' an carry on till bowt levun ... then he start slowin' up. Iyd be way ahid o'him, an I hatter stop so he'd ketch up. 'Sheez a back-brearkin' owd job!' I say. 'She bludder is!' he say, 'she bludder is!' I tell 'im streart... we wunt dew't less we wuz forced tew. No more we wunt, would we?

No, bor, that we wunt. Wass tyme o'yeer I rekun. Ent no wasser tyme o'yeer fer gorn arter the beet when yer hands is tew frooz ter howld them leaves.

No, an I towld 'im that anorl.

Wod he say?

He say suffin bowt bein ortermaytun.

Woss wun o'them, then?

He say thass merkanical hoss or suffin ... an by Christ he needed wun o'them tyme he'd dun that day!

Bet he liked Lunnun arter that!

Yeh ... They ent used ter it, yer know. They dunt know wot hard wakk is up Lunnun.

Somewhere in the clear autumn sky two jet planes chased and wooed each other, scattering the surprised but patient birds out of their tree-top nests. From the distance came the slow sound of a tractor bringing the cart and more men to top and take away the knocked beet. A third of the large field was brown now; a trampled, muddy shore bordering the sodden, sea-green beet. The two soaked men stood a minute in front of the new row and surveyed what they had done and what they would do.

Thass the tew-earker dun now, entit?

Yeh. An we'll be up this here row an down the next afore dinner tyme.

Yeh.

'Ewsed only ter dew row an'harf long o'him, thow. Wunce, we took tew hour ter dew wun row, an at end o'that he say, 'Iym finishin' arter this row. Buckley kin tearke tyme orff mer pay.' I say ter him' 'Yew unt ever git ewsed tew't if yer give up.' He say, 'Iyll git ewsed tew't ... in small doses. But Iyre hed nuff fer terday' he say. 'Woss matter, bor?' I say. He say, 'I ent no cop ter yew, slowin' yew up. That wearste farmer's tyme anorl, an I wunt be ner ewse ter mesself afore long' he say. 'Yew dunt wotter worry abowt me, ole partner' I say ter him. 'Cors Iyll go farster 'an yew. Stand ter reesun. Iym moor ewsed tew't an wot yew are, bor. Wuh, me bein sixter an yew twetty dunt mearke ner diffrunce' I say. 'Yew dunt wotter tearke no notice o'me if I go quicker 'n' yew. Blarst, thass only nattrel.' He wuz on orl fours on the ground, he wuz. Coont move. He keep gittin' up, yer see. Well, that dunt dew ter keep gittin' up, dew't?

165

No, that dunt .. no, that dunt.

An I tell'im that anorl! I say 'Yew dunt wotter keep gittin' up. I know yew wont tew sumtymes. We orl dew. Blarst, nun onus kin keep gorn wi'owt gittin' up now an' agin.' An nor we carnt, kin we? 'But yew ... yew stand up evra minnit!' I say. 'Yew dunt wotter dew that; that dunt mearke yer feel ner better forrit. Thass rum job I know ter stay down when yew wotter git up. But yew keep gorn, ole partner, jist yew keep gorn. Yew'll git ewsed tew't. Yew'll git ewsed tew't, yew wunt notise noffin' I say ter him.

Dew he pack up, then?

No, he dint. We hev hour left an he pick hisself up an pull a fearse an carry streart on. Ryte slow, mynd yer. But he go on fer bowt twetty minnits. He stop ... but he dunt lift his back. Nut wunce. He lean on his knees an he sit on his hornches wi' his back bent, or he jist stop an dunt knock. But fer bowt twetty minnits he jist dint lift his back. Then he stop harfway up the row an he sit down on that muck an he look sorter sad. Then he git up agin an start hittin' them bloomin' beet ser hard! Blarst me, wunce he miss an knock hisself clean orff his feet! Come four o'clock he look fit ter drop.

Ennywun else wi'yer?

There wuz him an me knockin ... a Harry, Jarge, Willy a Monty toppin. When we wuz dun, owd Monty, he come ter this here chap and he say ter him 'Blarst me! Yew look's thow you're hed 'nuff far the day!' An he say,'Yeh, rekun I hev!' An Monty, he say, 'Wot yew want now is ter tearke yew a mawther, bowt sixteen or seventeen... thass wot yew want now.' This young feller, he say, 'That seem ter me thass your remerdee fer evrathing rownd here.' And Monty, he say, 'So that is, bor ... so that is!' He say, 'Yew wotter tearke har till har hairpins stand on ind!' He's rum lad, owd Monty. He go arter the bit when he want tew, dunt he?

Yeh,

Yeh.

A dog sniffed in crazy circles after what he thought was a rabbit, and the dull thud, thud, thud of the earth being knocked off the beet was a continual background rhythm to the flat land's quiet noises. The air was heavy with late warmth.

That wotter be lyke this here orl the tyme, dunt it?
Yeh, fair owd job, this here.
Yeh. Go on orl day lyke this.
Yeh …
Yeh …

It was a rich and satisfied Norfolk countryside, worked and worn.
And where the earth had already been ploughed up after the harvest,
it seemed as if the land were yawning, very, very tired.

A break for five sugar beet workers in the 1950s at Calthorpe, near
Aylsham; (l to r) Titch Lambert, Joe Flowerdew, Jack Goodwin, Stanley
Norman and Pat Dennis.

Tony Clarke

SMOCK TACTICS

Tony Clarke lived life at the double as respected journalist and rustic joker. There may have been occasions when one demanding role spilled over into the other- although there are no confirmed reports of him attending a full council meeting in smock, chummy hat and boots with string round his trouser legs 'to keep varmints out from playing havoc with the future of England.'

When he died at 71 in 2008, a bright light went out across the Waveney Valley, the area he loved and served with such distinction as the *Eastern Daily Press* chief reporter at the Beccles office for quarter of a century.

I first met him in the late 1960s when he shone as 'Spigot', combing Wymondham and district for all the news fit to print in the old *Norwich Mercury* weekly newspaper. His diligent approach and gentle humour characterised a long career at the heart of community events involving people and places he knew well.

We resumed our cheerful links as Tony's masterly creation, the Boy Jimma, became a regular member of my Press Gang troupe of local entertainers in the 1990s. Tony pointed unashamedly to his countryman's smock as a key component in Jimma's surge to fashionable status.

'It came into my possession at a time during my youth when that great smock-class humorist Sidney Grapes was in his prime and my personal ambition was to become either a clergyman or a comedian. Cracking jokes while wearing a garment resembling a surplice seemed the ideal compromise while I earned a living as a journalist with the *EDP*' he told me after one laughter-soaked outing.

More sweet echoes to come from the path trodden over a half century earlier by the Boy John, alias Sidney Grapes, who made his mark as a local comedian before writing a series of celebrated dialect letters to the *EDP*. Like his much-loved predecessor, Boy Jimma burst into colourful print after a long and jovial apprenticeship on stage.

Two volumes of homely memoirs, *Mighta Bin Wuss* and *Thass A Rum Ow Job*, proved how the pen can be just as mighty as the boards when it comes to spreading a cultural gospel. Tony's madcap scripts for annual off-the-cuff pantomime productions by Friends Of Norfolk Dialect enhanced a glowing reputation for catching the vernacular delightfully in print and on stage.

Boy Jimma certainly took his time (and a fair bit of the audience's as well) as he related yarns steeped in old country ways, many of them emanating from his proud family motto: 'That sometimes pay yew to look sorfter than yew really are.'

He had an endearing habit of interrupting himself with some rogue observation and then asking the audience, or even the cast, where he had got to in his riveting discourse. This could add several minutes to his allotted span. We knew he had by no means finished as he prefaced another lengthy episode with an intake of breath and an elongated 'Ennyhow...'

Now and again as the village hall clock raced ahead I resorted to tugging Jimma's smock from the back in a subtle hint to wrap up. He would turn round slowly, grin, wink and return to his adoring followers with an apology for being interrupted in full flow.

On what proved to be his final Press Gang outing at Walsingham in September, 2006, I noted on my running order; 'Not so much a slow-burn delivery as an eventual-singe.' Jimma provided scope for such deep musing on a Saturday night.

Despite those periods of extra time – and Jimma was by no means the only Press Gang comic to sail way past his tell-by date – our rustic rambler is recalled with enduring affection and amusement by those able to keep pace with his whimsical slant on a way of life fast fading into the sunset.

Jimma's stories underlined his vulnerability (and ours) in the face of a world often short on understanding and compassion. Therein rested much of their humour. A simple trust in human nature allied to an innate sense of goodness had to bring just rewards ... eventually.

Many of those yarns found permanent homes in the two books Boy Jimma produced with a little help from Tony Clarke, a double act that lit up the Waveney Valley and far beyond.

Here are a few examples to help admirers remember them both for the best part of some time.

MIGHTA BIN WUSS

Jimma was a sickly child, as many were in his day. But our hero was sickly in more ways than one, sick of body and wayward of mind.

'He mearke everybody sick, he do,' his father was heard to observe with notable lack of sympathy.

They were a poor family, but proud. So poor that they could not afford respectable clothes for a growing infant. So proud that, inadequately attired as he invariably was, Jimma was never allowed out in public.

Indeed, he was four years old before the family could afford to buy him a hat which covered his head decently enough for him to be seen looking out of the window.

On one occasion as a baby – and only one – was he decked out in the finest clothes which his family had borrowed so that he would have his photograph taken with 'one o'them new fangled camera things.'

The problem was that the only people who could be persuaded to lend Jimma's parents the necessary baby clothes for the photograph were an elderly couple who had been very proud of their baby daughter.

She had grown up into 'a slummeken grit mawther' but they had kept her baby clothes as a reminder of what a bonny baby she had been.

'That dornt matters whether the garmints were mearde fer a boy or a gal' say Jimma's mother. 'They look noice an' at his earge he won't know the diff'rence.

'Anyhow,' she added as an afterthought, 'I wus really hooping fer a pretty little mawther, and blast if that dint tarn out ter be Jimma.'

* * *

The cottage which Farmer Greengrass had set aside for Jimma and Liza was only sparsely furnished, and after several months of hard saving they decided to go to the nearest town to buy some chairs. 'I dunt want any ow rubbish, even though we are hard up' said Jimma. 'You want stuff ter last. I fancy some o'them anteeks if they dunt corst tew much.'

'My father allus reckon yew carnt dew better than a good anteek' he said, warming to his subject. 'They're owd and they're well mearde an' yew c'n allus find ways a-mearkin' 'em larst a bit longer.'

'Father ha got a ow anteek in his shud. Thass his pride an' joy. Thass a owd axe an' thatta bin handed down in our family fer generearshuns.

Thass so owd Father're hed ter fit two new hids and three new handles in the time he're had it, so goodness know how many thet hed afore that come ter 'im.'

* * *

It had taken some time for the war to make an impact on life in Jimma's village. Being in a reserved occupation, as a producer of food, he escaped an early call to arms. Instead, he joined the Local Defence Volunteers, who later became the Home Guard, meeting once a week in the village hall for drill night and taking part in exercises at the weekends.

In the early years weapons were few and far between, the platoon's meagre arsenal consisting of a few 12-bore shotguns, a couple of .22 rifles and a first world war officer's pistol which had belonged to Lord Wymond-Hayme, who inevitably became commanding officer.

'How d'yer think yer a-gorn ter stop them Jerries wi that lot?' the gal Liza asked Jimma one night after drill. 'People say they're got a lot more stuff than yew lot hev.'

Jimma's face took on a conspiratorial look. 'Yew din't orta arst questions,' he said. 'I aren't at liberty ter gi' yer orl the informearshun on account of thass a secret, so his Lordship say.

'We dunt want details o' our defensive arrearngements a gittin inter the lugs o'the enemy,' explained Jimma. 'They're got spies everywhere, so he rekon.'

'But I aren't a enemy!' protested Liza. 'Surely yew c'n tell me suffin. I aren't a-gorn to go blarin thet out ter no Jarman spies.'

'Well, I'll jist say this,' replied Jimma mysteriously. 'That orl depend on us hidin' in the woods and dewin suffin called gorilla warfare.'

'Blast thass a rummun,' remarked his wife, none the wiser. She said no more but she was puzzled. Somebody had told her that all kinds of monkeys, including gorillas, lived on bananas and you couldn't get a banana for love or money during the war.

Anyway, she never knew gorillas could shoot. And, while they was on the subject, how come Jimma always took his darts to drill nights? Surely he wasn't going to throw them at the advancing Jerries?

She gave up. The Official Secrets Act was obviously a particularly impenetrable piece of legislation in wartime.

THASS A RUM OW JOB!

Jimma's son Fred – who will hereafter be referred to as Young Jimma to avoid confusion and to stick with family tradition – was as weedy a child as his father had been.

He also showed a similar lack of enthusiasm for school work, although he had inherited his father's love of nature and the countryside. This caused him to spend much of his time at school gazing out of the window of what he regarded as the prison of his classroom.

'He's just like his father,' commented Ernest Swishem, now a portly figure of considerable authority in the village and nearing the end of his long career as village schoolmaster.

'He's tew bricks short of a load, if yew arst me,' he added in accents which showed how 30 years in Jimma's village had undermined the origins of clarity in his diction.

* * *

Edie wrapped her eager arms around Ow Jimma and their lips met in a shuddering kiss which seemed to last forever. A strange sensation rippled through Jimma's ageing body.

Eventually Edie came up for air. 'Blast if I know!' she exclaimed. 'Yew hent harf improved since yew wus a boy. That kiss sent a shiver up an' down my spine.'

'Thass probly 'cos this hare fence what we're up agin wunt electrified in them days,' said Jimma, suddenly aware that the strange sensation had been inspired by the low current in the wire which passed along the fence. Sadly, it was not a sign of an awakening libido. 'The farmer ha' gotta keep the cows in the fild somehow,' he said.

'Never mind what that wus,' said Edie 'Let's try it agin.' And they did, with the same result. 'That don't harf remind me o' wen I wus young' said Edie. 'I think we orta git tergether agin of a Wensdy afternune.'

* * *

On an impulse he decided to take a short cut through the churchyard. As he walked along the path he caught sight of a figure lying prostrate on one of the tombstones.

At first he thought it was a stone angel until he realised the figure was in a far-from-angelic pose, and it was actually moving.

Perhaps this was a drunk, thought Arnie. Or somebody who was overcome with grief. Either way, he might be in need of help and Arnie was a kind-hearted boy.

As he approached a low moan escaped from the mournful figure. 'Why did yew hatta die?' it sobbed. 'Why did yew hatta die?'

Arnie took pity and bending over the man, laid a hand on his shoulder. 'Is that the grearve of yar beloved missus?' he asked kindly.

'No,' said the man, turning round to reveal the most pitiful of tear-stained faces. 'Thass har fust husband a-lyin' in thare!'

* * *

'I went ter King's Lynn on the bus larst week to dew some shoppin',' said Sarah. 'My Wally hed arst me ter gorn buy him some red an' white spotted paint an' a bag o'rubber tin tacks.

'That wus his idea of a jook,' she added unnecessarily. 'Even arter we're bin tergether orl these years he still think I'm sorft.'

'Anyway, the ironmongers wus sellin' them new type o'toilet brushes wi' the stiff bristles, so I bought tew on'em.'

'Oh, ah,' said Mother. 'How are yew gittin on with 'em?'

'Well, I keep a parseverin',' replied Sarah. 'But my Wally ha' give up on 'em an' gone back ter usin' pearper!'

* * *

One day, as he sat beside the river watching his float, an empty tin by his side, a boat full of holiday tourists pulled into the bank and moored.

To all appearances, Jimma was asleep, his head nodding forward, his mind dwelling on happy memories of an eventful life. 'Look at that poor old yokel' said one of the holidaymakers. 'He's been nowhere, done nothing and he looks as if hasn't got two pennies to rub together, poor old sod.'

Taking pity on the apparently poverty-stricken old fisherman, the holidaymaker walked up to him and placed a pound coin in his tin. Then, pausing, he concluded that the old man might be lonely. He would engage him in conversation – and maybe poke a little fun at him. He wouldn't know. He was too simple, of course.

'Have you caught many today?' the holidaymaker asked in mock-friendly tones. Jimma pocketed the pound coin, looked up at the stranger, smiled his gappy smile and said: 'I reckon yew're about the fourth!'

THE MEETING PLACE

Just as the big two market days were held regularly each week, Norwich on Saturday, Ipswich on Tuesday, so the little country towns surrounding our village had their own market day. Oscar and Ted always celebrated the occasion of Harleston market and usually met with their horses and carts at the 'Cherry Tree' in preparation for their weekly speculation at the sale ground.

'See you next week, then Oscar, bor' said Ted as they parted company outside the 'Fox' on a Saturday night.

'Yes,' said Oscar, 'I should be there if the ow mare is all right, only I ant sure what time I can git there.'

'Ow,' said Ted. 'How shall I know if yere ahid ar me or arter?'

'Well,' replied Oscar. 'You know that white gate at the top a' the hill. If you git there first, you put a stone on top a' the post and if I get there first I'll knock it orf.'

Frank Etheridge., *Salt on a White Plate*, 1988

Michael Brindid

Elizabeth Austrin
(Gal Liza)

REVIVAL SPIRIT

One millennium ended and another began with heartening signs of the Norfolk dialect cause not just coming back into fashion but embracing new ways and means of staying there.

Friends Of Norfolk Dialect emerged in 1999 from a determination to put the fight on an official footing when it came to preserving and promoting this vital strand of local heritage. Suddenly, national television and radio productions wading in murky Mummerzet waters were held to account and offered expert advice on how to reach the shores of acceptability.

Some listened and learned – but too many seemed ready to carry on drowning in weak excuses about 'such a hard accent to do' and dismissive grunts aimed at 'that strange lot from Norfolk moaning again.'

Fully justifiable moaning must continue as a key plank in the FOND platform while such insulting behaviour persists among theatrical types who wouldn't dream of dropping Belfast voices into a play set in Dublin or confusing a Scouser with a Geordie or Adge Cutler with George Formby. Norfolk's glory in being different should be recognised and applauded by any who want to pay dramatic tribute.

Meanwhile, the number of enthusiastic natives and daring newcomers prepared to write and perform home-made dialect delights, most of them nodding gratefully towards stirring examples set on village hall stages before television started ruling so many lives, shows every sign of keeping that revival spirit on track.

Regular social events, known delightfully as FOND-dews, the annual festival celebration in Cromer and 'missionary' visits by hardened campaigners to give uplifting talks to local schools and various organisations play important parts in maintaining a high profile for a subject long deemed worthy of rising above the ' quaint little anachronism' level.

A couple of Broadland scribes picked up the Boy John baton with dialect letters to the *Eastern Daily Press* either side of the millennium landmark. Michael Brindid of Hickling, just a few salt breezes away from Boy John's base in Potter Heigham, regaled readers in the 1990s while Elizabeth Austrin of Stalham, switching easily into her guise of Norfolk mawther Gal Liza, took her turn in the early years of a new century.

Both proved how the unquenchable spirit and dry humour running through epistles printed in the same newspaper from 1946 until 1958, could still work their spell in fresh settings. In Michael's case, two best-selling books, *I Din't Say Nothin'!* and *I Din't Say Nothin'... Agin!* reminded us how items of temporary amusement could be transformed into collections of permanent value.

His wife Norah starred as the long-suffering 'Missus' in domestic bulletins from their Hickling home called Orfanon. (Sidney Grapes and wife Ella lived in a little flat above the garage in Potter Heigham. They called their abode Uptop). Michael died aged 71 in 1998 just as his second volume of letters reached the top of the local best-seller list.

Gal Liza, valued member of my Press Gang cast of travelling entertainers, also stayed close to home with monthly missives from her Stalham headquarters, Euneda House. Husband John joined her in keen support for Friends Of Norfolk Dialect as that body became firmly established. Liza's musical prowess shone through as she provided piano accompaniment for the annual pantomime fun.

Here are examples of letters spearheading the revival movement decades after Boy John's final Broadland bulletin appeared in the *Eastern Daily Press*:

MICHAEL BRINDID

THA OLE CHICKEN IS STILL COLD, SHE SAY – April, 1994

Hev yer got ter the stearte where you fergit things? If you hev, Mr Editor, then you'll know wat I'm on about. Like in yar orfice, I bet you say sumtoimes, 'Where's tha' latter I hed a minnit ago? Where's my pen?' or 'Hev enyone sin my car keys?'

Tearke my missus, tha' wus Motherin' Sunda, so she say, 'We'll hev a chicken fer our dinner.' She got everything riddy, put it in the ole oven wi' sum bearked teartus, then set the toimer. She say, 'Tha's all riddy. All I're gotter do is ter mearke the batter puddin' when I git home an' we'll hev a nice dinna.'

So me an' the missus went up ter the Motherin' Day Sarvice. There's sum lot o'people tan out fer tha'. They give all the mothers a little bunch o'flowers. They all loike tha' corse tha' mearke 'em feel suffen special – an' so they are.

Ennyhow, we git home, lookin' forward ter our dinna. The missus go inter the back plearce ter put har batter puddin' in. She cum inter the front room ter me. 'I're dun a job. I're fergot ter tan the oven on' she say. 'Tha' ole chicken is as cold now as it wus when I put it in.' She say, 'We'll hev it fer tea instead.' I say, 'No, my luv, bein's as Mother's Day I'll tearke you out ter dinna.' I hed to giv har a bar o' chocklet an' a packet o'crisps ter mark the occcairsion, but I thort hevin' someone cook dinna fer har would be nice.

'Well wa's wrong wi' tha'?' I hear you say. Hev you ever tried ter git a dinna on Motherin' Sunda wirrout a-bookin' fust? Well, bor, we went all over the plearce. Tha' wus a job. In the ind we got in a plearse at East Russen an' hed a nice meal. Arter dinna we had a look round Russen cors tha's where the missus lived afor I married har, an' tha's where we did our courtin'... but tha's enuff o' tha'.

Talkin' about fergittin, another thort a now cum ter me. My farther, he wus a carpenter afor me. He wus tellin' me about a blook he warked with who mearde a shud an' boarded it up all the way an' fargot ter leave a doorway' So tearke hart, Mr Editor, wen you do start ter fergit things – just remember tha' happens ter all on us at sum toime or other.

THE PLEARCE WUS IN AN UPROAR – March, 1995

I wus a-listenin' ter the City's match on the ole wireless a Saturda arternoon.

The missus wus hevin' har annual bath. She shouted: 'Are we a-gorn' out ternite?' I say, 'If yer want tew.' 'What dew yer think 1 oter wear?' she say. I say, 'Yew'll hatter put more on than yer got on now tha's fer sure.' She spent the next hour a-trickolairtin' harself up. She say ter me, 'Aren't yew a-comin' yit, tha's gittin dark alriddy.'

So we went round the cust ter Bacton. Wen we got there she reckoned she fancied a small harf. We stopped at a nice plearce and sat at a tearble near a winda tha' looked out ter sea. Not tha' we could see a lot corse tha' wus as black as the hairkes. She hed wot she wanted an' let me hev a glass o' wine, but unly one on account o' me a-drivin'. (Sumtimes I think tha'ud be nice if she could dew the drivin'!)

We stayed an' hed a little mardle then got in the car ter cum humm. She say, 'Dorn't go yit, I're left my gloves. I'll go back an' git 'em. Yew cum wi' me.' Wen we got ter the tearble where we'd bin a-sittin' sum more fooks sat there. The missus say, 'I're lorst my gloves, hev yew sin 'em?' They got up an' hed a look. The people at the next tearble did the searme. Afore long the plearce wus in an uproar with evryone a-lookin' fer har gloves. In the ind, the blook wot own the plearce cum uver. He say, 'Wus a-gorn on here?' The missus say, 'I're lorst my gloves.' He say, 'Leave it ter me, I'll git my clearners ter hev a look in the mornin' an I'll give yew a ring if they find 'em.'

She thort he wus ever ser nice.

On the way humm we stopped at Stallum fer fish an' chips. Tha' put har in a good mind. When we got humm she took har coat an' har little lambs wool hat orf. Yew're not gorn' ter believe this but har gloves war in the top o' the hat, so all the while we warr a-lookin' for 'em she was a-wearin' 'em on top o' har hid. Did yew ever know anyone ser sorft!

GAL LIZA

THE GOOD OLE LINEN PROP – February, 2004

Dear Sar,

I wunder how manya readers hev still got a linen prop? I mean the good ole-fashun wooden one.

What brort this ter moind wus I nearly tripped over moine tother day. Sarve me roite fer not putting it back where that belong, a'leanin agin the shud. Thass bin wi' me the best part o' fourta years. I kin tell yar thass dun a lot more things other than proppin up the linen line. Yis, I know some onyer wud say washin line but us Norfick folk call it linen.

Well, ter git back to the prop. We useter poke the apples orf the top o' the tree what we cudn't reach. O'corse they wus allus the biggest an' best wuns. That wus allus a job ter try an' catch 'em afor they hit the ground. Corse thass rescued manya ball from the branches as well.

When we wus farst married an' hed sum kindly nairbors they useter use the prop ter tap the upstairs bedrum winder if we wus lairte up. An' if I dint watch him the Boy John wud git hold o' that prop an' use that on the gaardin as a line for sewin his seeds. O'corse when I cum ter use that the muck wud cum orf all on mi linen.

Dew yew know we're still got our 'lectric wash boiler an' thass cumin up ter fourta six years old. Moind yew, that still cum out if we want ter boil a Chrismuss puddin or a crab. Boy John say yew hed betta tell 'em yew dornt still dew yar washin it it. I useter be right proud ter see mi whoites hangin on the line arter a good ole boil-up, an dint they smell lovla arter a good ole blow.

I must jest say 'How ya' gittin on mi ole bewties?' ter them Norfick folk what are livin abroard an' hev got ter know me thru mi letters in the pearper. Corse yew know the EDP kin travel a long way wi' the help o' famley an' friends. Keep yew a'spreadin the Norfick dialect – an' dew yew keep a'troshin, tergether.

Yars Fondly,

Gal Liza

PS... Sum folk speak from experience – an' sum from experience dunt say nothin.

Dear Sar,

What a bewtiful dair that wus fer Tunstead Trosh. Not a breath o'wind an' that ole sun shone.

We arrived an' stood gorpin acrorse the field. That brort back memrees watchin that ole reaper binder a'gorn along an' chuckin out shoofs o'corn.

That seemed loike enny minute out wud cum the bottle o'cold tea an' the wittles. There wus nothin loike it, sittin alongsoide o'the hidge wi' mi grandfather an' the rest onem when I wus a little'un. Manya toime mi grandmother hed mearde him a puddin boiled in a clorth.

Corse he'd shair it wi' me, cuttin that up wi' his shutknife he allus hed in his pocket. He wudda used that knife fer cuttin evrathing else wi' a quick wipe on his sleeve ter clean it. I dornt think that wud happen terdair, that wunt be roite fer them health an'sairfty folk.

That wunta bin The Trosh wi'out the soight an' smell o' the tracshun engine a'standin there tickin over wi' the ole belt slappin away. Corse all drivers allus hev that little bit o'clorth hangin outer thar pocket riddy ter give a little polish hare an' a little rub there. I wunda whether thar woives ever git that little bit o'clorth clean, or dew they allus hull it away? I wunt put it parst sum onem ter use thar neckerchief!

I met this hare chap I knew at skool an' he reckin he got lorst on the way. That wernt no good o'him arskin the way to The Trosh corse no wun dint understand him. Moind yew, he dew cum from tew villages away an' he tork proper loike what I dew!

Yars Fondly,
Gal Liza

PS … If things dornt chairnge, they'll probly stay the searme!

GAL JANIE REPORTS

October, 1952

Well, the club a-got orf to a fresh start agin. They a-got the sairme Prasident but the sackertery a-resigned, so they gathered up an' give her a handlebag. I rackon that was to sort o'encourage the new 'un an' keep her up to the job.

The Missus, she come home an' told us how they had a man a-talkin' to 'em all about what was in sausages an' that like. The Master, he say, 'Pore feller', he say, 'I rackon he don't fancy his grub much' he say, 'not if he know erzackly woss in it. I wonder what he'd a-made o' Mrs B's surprise pudden', he say. He 'on't never forget that. I thought at the time he would o'died of a perplexy. That was like this hare. Owl Mrs B, she allus mairke a steam pudden in a gret owl bairsin, then she sairve half on it to hot up the nexter day. She got this hare receipt outer a book, 'an time that was a-doin' she say, 'Thass hully riz up', she say, 'I rackon thass as light as a feather'. Then when she come to tarn it out, she found she'd left the dwile down-a the bottom o' the bairsin. My heart, she hully took on. Th' owl cat, that scrapped outer the way right quick, an' her owl man, he hatta set somewhat quiet till that blowed over. For two-tree weeks, he talk, he dassent hardly arst her what she got for dinner.

Suffin' else this hare man said, there's so many mice hairs in every pound o' flour an' they can't git 'em out. I wisht they'd leave things alone. We-a bin all right up to the prasent, but if they keep a-probin' into the grub an' a-findin all that there rubbitch, we'll all git pizened orf afore the crownairtion.

Fare ye well, tergether, an' be you careful what you eart.

GAL JANIE

(From "Darkest Norfolk" by Gal Janie. Published by the Norwich Business and Professional Women's Club)

DEW YEW LOOK UP!

We can't show yew a mount'n,
An, bor, we're short o'hills,
An' yew oon't taake long a'countin'
Ar caastles an' ar mills.
But don't yew set there sighin' –
Jus' caast yar oyes up high
Where clouds an' baads are flyin',
An' see ar Norfick Sky!

(John Kett)

FURTHER READING: NORFOLK DIALECT BOOKS

Books written about and in the Norfolk dialect remain extremely popular, although several have been long out of print. It is worth hunting round the shelves of secondhand bookshops in search of them, or try any of the second-hand book websites, and libraries are always ready to assist. It may also help to consult the popular Friends Of Norfolk Dialect website: www.norfolkdialect.com. There are many dialect articles to be culled from old copies of both the *Norfolk Magazine* and the *East Anglian Magazine*.

Here's a list of likely sources in alphabetical order:

Michael Brindid; *I Din't Say Nothin'!* – Norfolk dialect letters to the *Eastern Daily Press*, 1995, and *I Din't Say Nothin' Ag'in!* 1998, both published by M Brindid and produced by Jim Baldwin, Fakenham.

Broad Norfolk; being a series of articles and letters reprinted from the *Eastern Daily Press*. Published 1893 by Norfolk News Co., Norwich, editor Harry Cozens-Hardy.

Bruther Will; *Norfolk Tales* published by Minimax Books, 1981.

Tina Chamberlain; *I Sit Here Thinkun*, and *Um Stilla Thinkun*, poems published by the author, 2007. Also a CD, *Thinkun Out Loud*.

Tony Clarke; *Mighta Bin Wuss, tales of the Boy Jimma*, 1998, and *Thass A Rum Ow Job, more tales of the Boy Jimma* 1999. Nostalgia Publications.

W N Dew; *A Dyshe of Norfolk Dumplings*. First published in 1898 by Jarrold Publishers. Republished 1973.

East Anglian Verse, 1974, *East Anglian Reminiscences*, 1976 and *East Anglian Short Stories*, 1977, all chosen and edited by E A Goodwyn & J C Baxter; and published by The Boydell Press.

Ida Fenn; *Tales of a Countryman* – stories of the Boy Jimma in Norfolk dialect. Published 1973 by Geo R Reeve Ltd, Wymondham.

Robert Forby; *The Vocabulary of East Anglia*. Two volumes originally published in 1830. Reprinted 1970 by Latimer Trend & Co. Ltd.

Eric Fowler (who wrote under the pseudonym of Jonathan Mardle); *Broad Norfolk*, Written by the readers of the *Eastern Daily Press*, 21 January – 19 March, 1949. Published 1949. *Broad Norfolk* published in 1973 by Wensum Books of Norwich.

Edward Gillett; *The Song o'Sorlomun in the Norfolk Dialect*. From the authorised English Version. First printed 1861, published 1862 by Thew, King's Lynn. Republished 1993 by Larks Press, Guist Bottom, East Dereham.

Sidney Grapes; *The Boy John Letters*. First published in volume form by Norfolk News Co. 1958. Published by Wensum Books, 1974. New edition by Mousehold Press, 2003, with two CDs of the letters read by Keith Skipper.

Ashley Gray; *Albie's Poems*, Reflections of a Norfolk Lad, published by George Reeve, Wymondham, 2007.

Lilias Rider Haggard (Editor); *I Walked By Night*, being the life and history of the King of the Norfolk Poachers. First published in 1935 by Nicholson and Watson, London. She also edited *The Rabbit Skin Cap*, a tale of a Norfolk countryman's youth. First published 1939. Reprinted by the Norfolk Library, 1974, 1975, 1976.

David Holbrook; *Getting It Wrong with Uncle Tom*, a Norfolk Idyll, Mousehold Press, 1998

John Kett; three volumes of dialect poems; *Tha's a Rum'un, Bor*, 1973, *Tha's a Rum'un Tew*, published in 1973 by Baron Publishing, Woodbridge, and *Watcher Bor* published by Wensum Books, 1979.

Robin Limmer; *Norfolk Dialect and its Friends*, John Nickalls Publications, 2009

Robert Malster; *The Mardler's Companion, a Dictionary of East Anglian Dialect*, Malthouse Press, 1999.

Mary Mann; *The Fields of Dulditch*, first published in 1902. Reissued 1976 by Boydell Press, Ipswich, and *Tales of Victorian Norfolk*, published by Morrow and Co., Bungay, 1991. Recently reprinted by Larks Press – *The Complete Tales of Dulditch*, *The Parish of Hilby*, *The Patten Experiment*, *Rose at Honeypot* and *Astray in Arcady*.

John Greaves Nall; *Glossary of the Dialect and Provincialisms of East Anglia*, originally published in 1866 by Longmans, Green, Reeder and Dyer, London. Reprinted by Larks Press, 2006.

Old Barney; A series of broadcasts on *BBC Radio Norfolk* in three volumes edited by Keith Skipper: *Dew Yew Keep a' Troshin'*, 1984, *Down at the Datty Duck*, 1985, and *Dunt Fergit Ter Hevver Larf*, 1986. All published by Jim Baldwin, Fakenham.

Colin Riches; Bible stories in the Norfolk dialect, *Dew Yew Lissen Hare*, published 1975 by George Nobbs Publishing, and *Orl Bewtiful an' New*, published 1978 by F Crowe & Sons, Ltd., Norwich.

Walter Rye; *Glossary of Words Used in East Anglia*, published 1895 for the English Dialect Society by Henry Frowde, Oxford University Press.

Keith Skipper; *The Norfolk Companion*, Jim Baldwin Publishing, 1994, *Larn Yarself Norfolk*, a comprehensive guide to the Norfolk Dialect, Nostalgia Publications, 1996, *Hev Yew Gotta Loight, Boy?*, the life and lyrics of Allan Smethurst, The Singing Postman, Countryside Books, 2001.

James Spilling; *Giles' Trip to London*, first published by Jarrold Publishing, 1872. Facsimile edition in 1998.

Beryl Tooley; *John Knowlittle*, The Life of the Yarmouth Naturalist, Arthur Henry Patterson, Wilson-Poole Publishers, 1985. *Scribblings of a Yarmouth Naturalist*, published by Beryl Tooley, 2004.

Peter Trudgill; *The Norfolk Dialect*, Poppyland Press, Norfolk Origins series, 2003

B Knyvet Wilson; *Norfolk Tales and Memories*, published 1930, *More Norfolk Tales and Memories*, 1931, both published by Jarrold and Sons Ltd. New version of both volumes in *Norfolk Tales* from Prospect Press in 2005. Revised and edited by George Nobbs.

Arnold Wesker; *The Wesker Trilogy*, including *Roots* (set in Norfolk) published 1984 by Penguin Books Ltd., Harmondsworth, Middlesex.